Geologists' Association Guide No. 46

CW00688079

Edited by
J. T. Greensmith

Notes. *The details of routes given in these guides do not imply a right of way. The onus of obtaining permission to use footpaths and to examine exposures rests with the user of the Guides who should observe carefully the Code for Geological Field Work issued from the Librarian. The Geologists' Association, c/o Department of Geological Sciences, University College London, Gower Street, London WC1E 6BT.*

In particular, those in charge of parties should ensure that there is no indiscriminate hammering of, or collecting from, exposures and that no damage is caused to property.

Any information (e.g. change in footpaths, filling in of quarries, threat to SSI's, new exposures) that would update and improve a revised edition of this guide would be welcomed by the Association.

PREFACE

The Isle of man has fascinated me for years and I have visited it for nearly 30 years, several times as the leader of a students' field course. With its wide variety of geological features, mostly well exposed and easily accessible on foreshores, students and leader alike have found the island highly instructive. It has been a surprise that so few geologists go there and so little is known of the story it has to tell.

The only comprehensive publication directly on the geology is Lamplugh's Geological Survey Memoir of 1903, now long out of date and difficult to obtain. A more up to date but condensed account is in Robinson & McCarroll's review of the geography, geology, archaeology, history and social geography (1990). Neither of these works is a guide book and no such publication has been traced. The only guides available are confined to the Quaternary sections (e.g. Dackombe & Thomas, 1985).

The present guide is presented in the hope that with its aid more geologists will discover the island and its geological attractions. It deserves to be better known both for its teaching qualities and its research possibilities. With the lack of even a general up to date work on the geology of the whole island, a somewhat longer introduction than is usual in guide books is given here, together with a select bibliography.

The sections herein concerning the Manx "slate" lean heavily on the work of Dr A. Simpson, formerly of Birkbeck College: he is too ill to take any part in the preparation of this guide but his published works have proved invaluable.

The writer would like to acknowledge the help he has received over the years from his erstwhile research student, David Quirk, from Tony Dickson for allowing the material in his thesis to be updated for publication, from Geoff Thomas who showed him the Pleistocene sections, from Dr Larch Garrad of the Manx Museum for her help and interest and from Trevor Greensmith for initiating the whole project.

The line-drawings are the skilful and patient work of Colin Stuart of the Department of Geological Sciences, University College London.

Trevor D. Ford

INTRODUCTION

Lying in the northern Irish Sea the Isle of Man is an island some 45 km long by 16 km wide (Figure 1). It is mountainous with peaks along its axis culminating in Snaefell at 621 m above sea-level. The Isle is a holiday resort with a somewhat Victorian flavour, including both steam and electric railways, and a mountain railway up the highest peak, Snaefell. The Isle of Man is a self-governing community with its own Parliament (Tynwald and the House of Keys), having been part of a Norse empire until the 13th century; many of its people still claim descent from the Vikings, whose tongue is reflected in the Manx language, now little used except for place names. The Manx government now pays allegiance to the Crown, who appoint a governor. The Manx people do not elect MPs to the House of Commons. Instead they elect their own parliament, the House of Keys. The Isle of Man has its own currency which is used interchangeably with British money, but letters posted on the Isle must bear Manx stamps.

The Isle of Man has a resident population of some 65,000 mainly occupied in farming, tourism and, in recent years, offshore financial companies. Liberal tax laws have made the Isle something of a tax haven and financial centre.

Access to the Isle is by ferry from Heysham to Douglas (in 3¾ hours each way), with less frequent services to Liverpool, Fleetwood, Belfast and Dublin (write to the Isle of Man Steam Packet Co. Ltd., P.O.Box 5, Douglas, for details). Alternatively one may fly to Ronaldsway airport from Blackpool, Liverpool, Manchester, Belfast, Dublin, Leeds, Birmingham, Glasgow and London (Heathrow); (details from Manx Airlines, Ronaldsway Airport).

Topographically the Isle of Man has a mountainous axis, split by a central valley from Douglas to Peel, with wide rolling plains to both north and south of the mountains. Both west and east coasts are rugged, but the north and south coasts are more gentle. The Calf of Man is an island off the southern tip, now a bird sanctuary. There is a wealth of archaeological relics dating mainly from Neolithic, early Christian and Norse times, with two mediaeval castles. On clear days viewpoints on the higher ground may permit one to see distant views of the Lake District, southern Scotland, Northern Ireland and, exceptionally, North Wales. These give room for speculation about what lies beneath the intervening sea floor; ferries from both Heysham and Liverpool pass fairly close to the Morecambe Bay gas field platforms, which produce gas from Permo-Triassic formations lying beneath much of the northern Irish Sea.

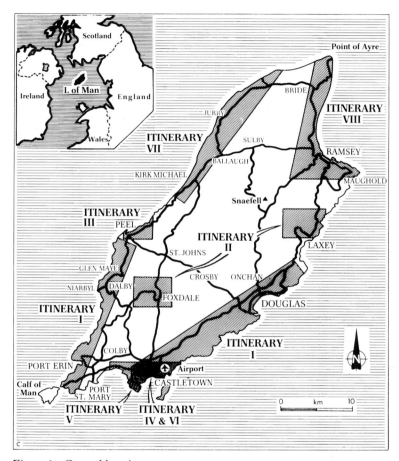

Figure 1: General location map.

GEOLOGICAL OUTLINE

About two thirds of the Isle of Man is composed of the Manx Group largely of Lower Ordovician age (Figure 2); commonly known as the Manx Slate, these rocks include various other rock-types and are here formalized as the Manx Group. The outcrops, particularly the cliffs of both coasts, provide ample opportunity for study of a thick pile of clastic sediments which have suffered multiple phases of deformation. The slates and associated rocks are intruded by three small Caledonian granite masses at Foxdale, Oatlands and Dhoon, and there is a scatter of minor intrusions, including the Poortown gabbro near Peel and numerous greenstone and lamprophyre dykes. Several mineral vein complexes cut both slates and granites and rich mines have yielded considerable quantities of lead, zinc, copper and some silver, principally at Laxey, Foxdale and Bradda Head, near Port Erin. Iron ore mines occur around Maughold Head in the northeast.

Immediately north of Peel is the coast section of the Peel Sandstones (Figure 2); almost certainly of Old Red Sandstone age, they are seen only in faulted contact with slates of the Manx Group or covered with Pleistocene deposits.

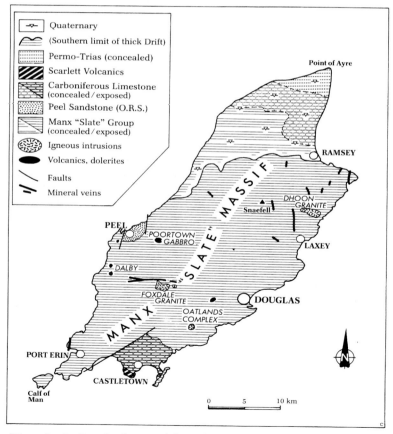

Figure 2: Outline sketch map of the geology of the Isle of Man.

The south coast has magnificent sections in the Carboniferous Limestone extending some some 10 km from Port St Mary to Castletown and Ronaldsway (Figure 2), including thin bedded limestones with abundant corals and highly fossiliferous "reef" build-ups. Associated conglomerates occur on the Langness peninsula, and the Scarlett Volcanic Formation occupies a 1.5 km section of coast west of Castletown, with many instructive examples of eruptive rocks.

Both Lower Carboniferous and Permo-Triassic strata are present but entirely concealed beneath Pleistocene deposits at the northern end of the Island.

A swarm of Tertiary dykes is to be found along much of the Island's coastline, and they are particularly well seen cutting the Carboniferous Limestone sections along the south coast.

The northern plain and the Bride Hills are underlain by Pleistocene glacial and associated deposits and the two coasts provide some 25 km of almost continuous exposures in these.

The Isle of Man has magnificent geology but has been generally neglected by geologists. A comprehensive account of the geology was given in the Geological Survey Memoir by Lamplugh (1903) based on his 1 inch to 1 mile map (1898) (recently reprinted on a 1:50000 scale by the British Geological Survey), though it is out of date in many respects. A series of papers by A. Simpson (1963-1968) updated much of the information on the Manx slates. Recently a summary of the geology has been provided by Dackombe (in Robinson & McCarroll's review of the geography, history and economy of the Isle of Man, 1990). Much of the geology can easily be seen in coastal sections and student parties have found these highly instructive; sections in folded and variously metamorphosed slates and greywackes of Lower Ordovician age, in Devonian (Old Red Sandstone) sediments, locally highly contorted, in various facies of Lower Carboniferous (Dinantian) limestones, in basaltic volcanics and dykes, and long sections in glacial and related sediments provide a good mixture of instructive geology, with few of the constraints facing much mainland geology today. Provided Geologists' Association members keep an eye on tides, they can have at least a week's good geology mainly on foreshores and below low cliffs. The few significant inland exposures can be left for high tide periods. Visits during the periods of the main motorcycle races are not recommended as certain main roads are closed to all traffic for several hours each day (TT races in mid June; Manx Grand Prix in late August).

The Manx Museum in Douglas has recently been re-organized and provides a useful introduction to the island's geology, natural history and particularly archaeology as well as to the unusual history. In conjunction with the Museum, the Manx National Trust administers a variety of sites and small museums throughout the island.

THE MANX GROUP

Although commonly referred to as the Manx slates, true roofing slates
are rare owing to the dominance of greywackes (a variety of sandstone)
in the sequence and to the complexities of folding and cleavage.
Lamplugh's (1903) work on the Manx Slates Series (now the Manx
Group) was too early for him to have appreciated the subtleties of all the
structures involved, though he realized that the strata on opposing
coasts young inwards and that the east coast Lonan Flags and the west

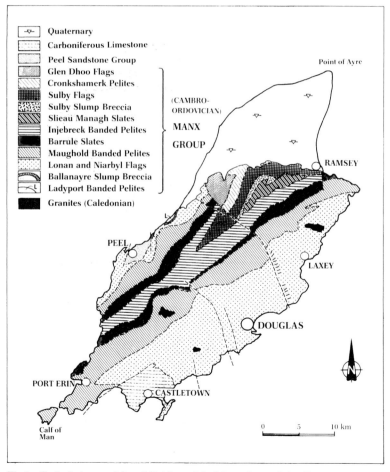

Fig 3: Geological map of the subdivisions of the Manx Group (after Simpson, 1963a).

coast Niarbyl Flags were stratigraphically equivalent yielding an overall synclinal structure. However, he over-generalized the structure of the main part of the slate outcrop as a classic concertina-like synclinorium. It is to Simpson (1963a) that we must turn for the only modern account and the only map of the subdivisions of the Manx Group (Figure 3). Even so, Simpson's work dates from before the concepts of plate tectonics and in particular of the Iapetus suture were known and some revision is probably necessary.

Sedimentology

Simpson recognized four different lithologies in the Manx Group:

1. Flaggy formations - siltstones, fine to medium greywacke, and subordinate pelite with some current and graded bedding and occasional slump folds (units 3, 9 & 11 in the list below)
2. Banded formations - composed of alternating bands usually less than 2 cm thick of dark blue pelite and pale or light grey siltstone, with some greywacke or quartzite beds (units 1, 4 & 6 in the list below)
3. Pelitic (shale/slate) formations - uniform dark blue or black pelite with some sandstone ribs (units 5, 7 & 10 in the list below)
4. Slump breccias - the results of subaqueous slumping with fragments of slate, siltstone and greywacke up to 7 cm wide embedded in dark pelite (units 2 & 8 in the list below).

Stratigraphy

On the basis of the above lithologies Simpson (1963a) mapped eleven stratigraphic units (herein regarded as Formations in accordance with the Rules of Stratigraphical Nomenclature) (Figure 3):

11.	Glen Dhoo Flags	(975m; 3200ft)
10.	Cronkshamerk Shales	(460-560m; 1580-1850ft)
9.	Sulby Flags	(640m; 2100 ft)
8.	Sulby Slump Breccia	(275-460m; 900-1500ft)
7.	Slieau Managh Slates	(335m; 1100ft)
6.	Injebreck Banded Pelites	(610-880m; 2000-2900ft)
5.	Barrule Slates	(160-925m; 530-3400ft)
4.	Maughold Banded Pelites	(790-1830m; 2600-6000ft)
3.	Lonan & Niarbyl Flags	(600-3000m; 2000-10000ft)
2.	Ballanayre Slump Breccia	(6-150m; 20-500ft)
1.	Ladyport Banded Pelites	(120m; 400ft)
		Total over 8000m; 25000ft.

Trevor D. Ford

Figure 4: "Worm" trails - sole markings on the Lonan Flags, Marine Drive (locality I/2).

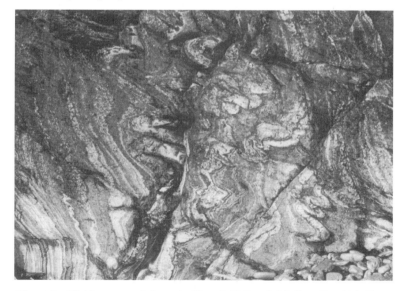

Figure 5: Highly contorted slump in Maughold Banded Pelites, Port Erin Bay.

Whilst a general similarity in both lithology and age to the slates of the Skiddaw Group of the Lake District is evident, as well as to the Leinster Group of southeast Ireland, no detailed comparison has been made. It seems likely that the base of the Manx Group may be somewhat older than the lowest Skiddaw Group, though both are now known to extend down at least into the Tremadocian (previously classed as upper Cambrian, but international rules now consider the Tremadocian as the lowest Ordovician subdivision).

The age of the Manx Group has been determined from limited palaeontological evidence. Trace-fossils of various sorts are to be found in most of the flaggy formations, but they tell us little about age (Figure 4). Two loose slabs with the dendroid graptolite *Dictyonema flabelliforme* (an invalid name according to some palaeontologists, now replaced formally by *Rhabdinopora socialis*), and *Dendrograptus flexuosus* were found by Bolton (1899) on Cronk Shamerk (Cronk Sumark on some maps) at the northern end of the slate massif. Further fragments were found by Rushton in 1992. These fossils suggest a Tremadocian age (i.e. lowest Ordovician). Fragmentary Didymograptid graptolites of probable Arenigian age were found in the Lonan Flags at Baltic Rock, east of Port Grenaugh (327703) in April 1992. Downie & Ford (1966) obtained uppermost Tremadocian to low Arenigian acritarchs from the Lonan Flags. In a more thorough study Molyneux (1980) obtained acritarchs from various flaggy formations at 22 localities from which he deduced that Formations 1 and 4 above were Arenigian in age, and 3 and 11 were Tremadocian. These dates contrast with the sequence proposed by Simpson so that some revision either of the stratigraphic sequence or of the acritarch dates is necessary. It may be either that strike-faulting and repetitions of parts of the sequence in the less well-exposed interior of the island were not recognized. In view of their similarity, it seems likely that the Glen Dhoo Flags are a faulted patch of Niarbyl Flags. The outcrops of the Ballanayre Slump Breccia and Ladyport Banded Pelites appear to be fault-bounded, so they may represent outliers of younger formations. Molyneux (1980) also noted that isolated exposures of sediments associated with the Peel Volcanic Formation (which Simpson regarded as part of the Niarbyl Flags) were late Arenigian or even early Llanvirnian in age. Though Simpson (1963a & 1968), following Lamplugh, regarded the Manx Group as older than the Skiddaw Group, subsequent views have suggested at least a partial equivalence and an outline lithological correlation has been proposed by Cooper and Molyneux (1990).

Palaeogeography

Whilst small-scale current and graded bedding and slump folds (Figure 5) are fairly common, little attempt has been made to determine the direction of transport for any of the 8000m of the Manx Group sediments and their relationship to Lower Ordovician palaeogeography remains uncertain. An unpublished undergraduate dissertation by J.B.McQuoid (University of Belfast) indicated that the Lonan Flags around Laxey were derived from the east-northeast, i.e. roughly along the axial trend of the later Manx syncline, though whether the same trend applies to the rest of the Manx Group sequence remains unknown. Dackombe (in Robinson & McCarroll, 1990) has suggested that the Manx Group is a turbidite mass with variations due to changes in source and direction of supply, with most having been deposited in a medial situation in a trough, being too fine-grained for a proximal situation and not fine-grained enough for a distal position.

On geophysical evidence, the Iapetus suture between the northern and southern British plates lay to the north of the Isle of Man and dipped southeastwards beneath the Isle in early Ordovician times. Both Manx and Skiddaw Group sediments could have been deposited in a fore-deep marginal to the southern plate. Derivation of sediments from the northern plate across Iapetus is unlikely as that ancient ocean was apparently still too wide in early Ordovician times.

Structure

The basic structure of the Manx Group massif is synclinal, but has resulted from three episodes of folding according to Simpson (1963a) (Figures 6, 7 & 8) :

F1 - an acute Manx syncline with a Caledonoid trend (NE-SW), with many subsidiary folds on its limbs, has its axis roughly along the western flank of the mountains; originally with a vertical axial plane, it has been refolded in the F2 phase on gently inclined fold axes. A stress field involving Caledonoid (NW-SE) horizontal compression was deduced. Most of the folds to be seen in the cliffs of the two coasts are small scale F1 folds (Figures 9, 10 & 11); they demonstrate that F1 was probably more complex as the degree and direction of plunge is highly variable.

F2 - refolding of existing structures was superimposed by this second phase, with more open folds having a Caledonoid strike but with axial planes dipping gently northwest, yielding the Manx synform (Figure 7). The F2 folding has resulted in the southeastern limb of the main F1 fold being partly inverted and dipping southeast. The stress field seems to have been imposed more or less vertically but with the same Caledonoid trend. Minor folds are scattered around the island (Figures 12 & 13).

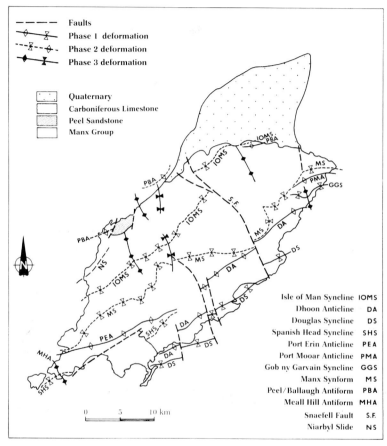

Figure 6: Sketch map of fold structures in the Manx Group (based on Simpson, 1963a).

F3 - several large cross-flexures have axial planes dipping steeply ENE. Their effect is to lift parts of the F1 and F2 structures to different levels in relation to the present day topography. The stress field seems to have been compressive at right angles to the Caledonoid axis. Kink bands related to F3 have been found in the northeast.

Each of the fold phases was accompanied by the development of cleavage, (S1, S2, & S3) parallel to the axial planes, with much adjustment by bedding plane slip. S1 is an axial plane flow cleavage;

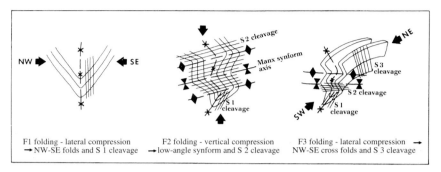

Figure 7: Diagram of the sequence of folding in the Manx Group (after Simpson, 1963a, and Robinson & McCarroll, 1990).

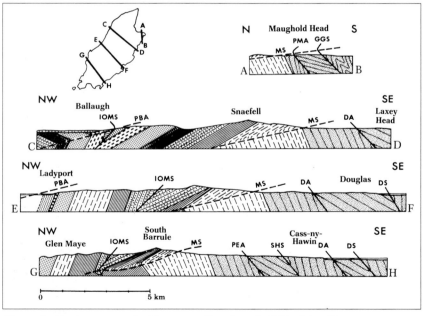

Figure 8: Sections across the Manx massif to show the folds (after Simpson, 1963a).

S2 is a crenulation cleavage parallel to the Manx synform axial plane, generally developed at a low angle (Figure 14); S3 is a second crenulation cleavage parallel to the F3 axial planes. Rod-like pencil slates are present where two or three cleavages intersect. Much quartz veining occurs in the axial belt of the island, particularly in association with F2 folding; the veins have been categorized as concordant (early F2), discordant (late F2), and irregular (mostly F3) (Simpson, 1963b).

Figure 9: View northeast along the cliffs north of Port Groudle, showing the nearly vertical Lonan Flags on the east flank of the Douglas syncline.

Figure 10: Lonan Flags standing vertical and younging to the left on the Marine Drive south of Douglas (locality I/2).

Figure 11: *F1 syncline in Niarbyl Flags, outside the walls of Peel Castle (locality I/10).*

Figure 12: *F2 fold in quartzites of the Maughold Banded Pelites, Cregneish quarry, Meall Hill.*

The trace of the axis of the Manx syncline is sinuous along the island and both this and complementary folds are offset in places by transcurrent faulting. The positions of the faults are mostly only known from mapping their effect on outcrop patterns, but one fault, the Niarbyl thrust, is demonstrable from the shearing and crush zone seen on the foreshore at Niarbyl Point. The axial plane trace of the Manx synform lies somewhat to the southeast of the synclinal axis, and it is similarly affected by faulting.

Figure 13: Vertical bedding in the Maughold Banded Pelites, Calf Sound (locality I/6).

The presence of three episodes of folding has been recognised in the Isle of Man, the Lake District and North Wales (Helm, *et al.*, 1963; Simpson, 1968). The latter proposed that phases F_1 and F_2 were directly related in the Isle of Man and the Lake District and that they must have taken place before the unconformable Borrowdale Volcanics were deposited on an eroded surface of the Skiddaw Group i.e. before the late Llanvirnian, though this interpretation was challenged in the discussion of Simpson's paper. A comprehensive comparison of the Manx and Lake District structures has still to be made and an analysis of the significance of these in terms of the closure of the Iapetus suture has yet to be done. The main metamorphism may have been as early as the F_2 fold phase though other opinion is that all the folding and metamorphism probably took place in late Silurian to early Devonian times.

Igneous Rocks

Contemporary volcanic rocks are present in the Manx Group at two localities, south of Peel and at Dalby. Exposures are very poor but there seem to have been short-lived outbursts of andesitic lava, tuff and agglomerate. Whether they can be regarded as early equivalents of the Eycott or Borrowdale volcanics of the Lake District is unknown. Contemporaneous intrusions include numerous "greenstone" dykes seen chiefly in coast sections (Figure 15). The dykes range in

*Figure 14:
Steeply dipping
Maughold
Banded Pelites
crossed by
nearly
horizontal S2
cleavage,
headland north
of Port Mooar.*

composition from augite diorite through camptonite to mica lamprophyre: the proportions of hornblende, augite and oligoclase feldspar are highly variable. Many of the dykes are altered to a calcite-chlorite rock. The dykes transect F1 folds but are often disjointed by the later tectonic episodes. There are also some larger basic masses, notably the augite gabbro at Poortown, near Peel (quarried by the Isle of Man Department of Highways, Ports and Properties, with samples common in carparks etc throughout the island), and a doleritic mass on the north side of Wills Strand, north of Peel. None of these igneous rocks has been studied in any detail since Lamplugh's Memoir (1903).

Some twenty microgranite dykes, porphyritic to varying degrees and usually referred to as porphyrites, are scattered mainly along the axis of the island (Simpson, 1964b).

Figure 15: Greenstone dyke in Maughold Banded Pelites, shore of Bay ny Carrickey.

Metamorphism

The greater part of the Manx Group outcrop falls within a low (chlorite) grade of metamorphism, i.e. greenschist facies. Textures and mineralogy increase in grade towards the axial zone, more or less in the same line as the axis of the Manx syncline (Figure 16). Simpson (1964a) deduced the presence the two phases of regional metamorphism, the first being syn-tectonic (F1), whilst the second included a zone of porphyroblasts along the hinge of the Manx synform (F2) dipping at a low angle towards the northwest. The porphyroblasts include leucoxene after ilmenite, muscovite, biotite, cordierite, garnet, chloritoid and tourmaline, suggesting that this axial zone may have just reached lower amphibolite facies. The F2 axial zone is characterized also by the development of much quartz veining in the slates (Figure 17). Contact metamorphism associated with the granites is superimposed on these two phases of regional metamorphism.

A recent study of mica crystallinity by Roberts et al. (1990) showed that the greatest crystallinity roughly coincided with Simpson's axial

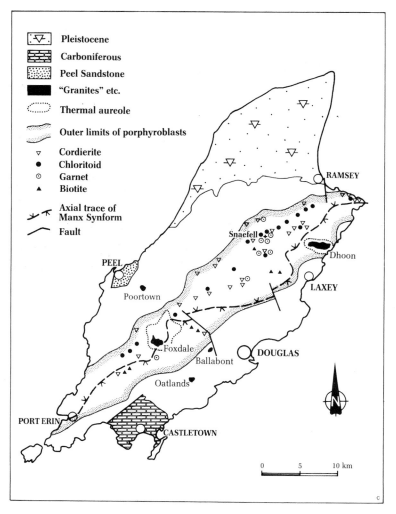

Figure 16: Sketch map of the metamorphism of the Manx Group (after Simpson, 1964a).

metamorphic belt; they also deduced that there had been two episodes of metamorphism, the first regional (largely anchizonal) associated with the folding, and the second a contact metamorphism around the granite intrusions, superimposed on the first.

Figure 17: Contorted quartz veining adjacent to the South Bradda Mine, Port Erin (locality I/7).

Age

Isotopic age determinations on various slates in the Isle of Man have yielded results as follows: 373 and 414 million years (Harper, 1966), and 370±5, 392±4, 390±7 million years (Ineson & Mitchell, 1979) all broadly "early Devonian", the time of the final closure of the Iapetus suture, and of both folding and metamorphism, not of sedimentation.

CALEDONIAN GRANITES

Outcrops of three small granitic intrusions occur in the axial region of the island at Foxdale and Dhoon; the Oatlands complex lies off the axis near the southeast coast (Figure 2). However, a gravity survey suggests that they are much more extensive in the subsurface. Each has its own lithological characteristics.

Foxdale

The granite outcrops on Stoney Mountain over about 2 square km and there is a small separate inlier at Eairy to the northeast. However, evidence from mines and the width of the metamorphic aureole indicate that it is present at shallow depth over about 10 square km (Simpson, 1965). Geophysical evidence suggests that the granite mass may be as much as 40 square km in area (Cornwell, 1972).The granite is moderately coarse-grained and non-porphyritic. Muscovite predominates amongst the micas and orthoclase in the feldspars. Very little is exposed of its contacts with the country rocks, a few xenoliths being seen in a stream bed south of Foxdale village. There are two quarries, one yielding fairly fresh rock, suitable for aggregate, whilst the other shows deeply weathered granite, so soft that it can be broken down by the fingers. This led to a short-lived attempt at exploitation with a primitive washing plant separating the crushed weathered granite into three products: quartz for mixing with cement for brick-making (there are no good quality brick clays on the island); feldspar for use in the Potteries, and mica for use by the roofing felt makers.

Figure 18: Foxdale granite cut by feldspar-rich pegmatite, in turn cut by a quartz-muscovite vein (locality II/1).

Crossing the granite outcrop in a NNW-SSE direction is a deep trench due to past and present workings of a "spar" vein. Spar in a Manx context is white quartz, usually with much mica, used widely as a rockery stone or for ornamenting the tops of walls and gateposts. The present spar quarry shows the vein to be a complex of several generations of pegmatite mutually cutting each other and cut by veins of almost pure quartz (Figure 18). The pegmatites contain variable proportions of quartz, feldspar and muscovite mica in crystals up to 10 cm wide sometimes showing striking graphic textures. Occasional vughs have freely grown crystals. There are rare occurrences of trace minerals such as beryl (Dawson, 1966).

The metamorphic aureole is up to 3 km wide, particularly around Archallagan (Simpson, 1965). Samples of hornfelsed schist may be found on the mine waste heaps, particularly at the old Cornelly Mine (295795), with small porphyroblasts of garnet, cordierite, staurolite and chiastolite in mica schist as typical material.

Simpson has been able to demonstrate from small-scale and micro-structures that the Foxdale granite was syn-tectonic, being emplaced during the F2 folding phase. It has been dated at 374±7 million years making it early Devonian in age (Brown, *et al.*, 1966).

Dhoon

The Dhoon granite, in the northeast of the island, was quarried until recently by the Department of Highways, Ports and Properties for road material. It is a fine-grained granodiorite with rather more biotite and plagioclase than the Foxdale granite; muscovite is uncommon. The granite is mostly porphyritic with quartz and feldspar phenocrysts up to 5 mm across. Quartz veins locally rich in tourmaline are found occasionally in the quarry. There appear to have been two phases of intrusion with an early darker, biotite-rich, phase now seen as an included mass within the later lighter phase. Numerous basic clots with biotite, sphene, ilmenite and apatite indicate absorption of basic xenoliths, as originally demonstrated in a pioneer study of magmatic contamination by Nockolds (1931). The presence of both steep shear joints and low-angle S2 fractures in the granite and the surrounding rock enabled Simpson (1964b) to demonstrate that the Dhoon granite was emplaced between tectonic episodes F1 and F2, somewhat earlier than the Foxdale granite, and that the granite was coeval with a microgranite dyke suite. An aureole 0.5 km wide surrounds the Dhoon granite, with pelites replaced by micaceous phyllites and quartz granulites.

Oatlands

The Oatlands complex in the southeast of the island is not on the main fold axis, but within the outcrop of the Lonan Flags. In spite of its small size, barely 0.5 square km, it was a complex intrusion, with a granite plug, largely quarried away, emplaced in the centre of a gabbro mass with an augite-rich ultramafic margin to the southwest. The contact zone of granite and gabbro showed numerous included blocks (xenoliths) of gabbro in granite and, further out, veins of granite penetrating the gabbro. The quarry has long been flooded and is now partly back-filled with rubbish so that there is little to be seen besides large blocks packed with xenoliths in various stages of digestion in nearby fields and walls (Taylor & Gamba, 1933). The structural relationship to the folding episodes is unknown.

The Foxdale granite has been dated at 374±7 million years, slightly less than the ages determined on the slates by Harper (1966) and Ineson & Mitchell (1979) which may indicate an approximation to the date of metamorphism as earliest Devonian. Dates around 320 million years obtained for the granites by Ineson & Mitchell (1979) are probably too low owing to argon loss. The relationship with the Dhoon granite and the folding episodes F1 and F2 confirms an early Devonian date for these parts of the Caledonian orogeny and thus makes it possible to relate them to the structural history of the final closure of the Iapetus suture.

MINES & MINING

The Isle of Man has a long history of metal mining with the earliest records of mining being in the 13th century. Stone hammers found on Bredda Head suggest even earlier, probably Bronze Age, mining. Relics of the extractive industries are widespread and a general account of their history has been given by Garrad et al.(1972). The Isle's largest tourist attraction today is the great Lady Isabella water-wheel erected at Laxey in 1854 as part of an elaborate scheme to keep the mines dry (Figure 21). Considerable restoration work has been done on the wheel and associated structures in recent years and a historical trail has been laid out (Cowin & Scarffe, c.1991).

The three main groups of mines (Figure 19) are at Laxey with the nearby Snaefell mine, at Foxdale with the associated Glen Rushen Mines, and at Bradda Head near Port Erin (Figure 20)(Lamplugh, 1903; Carruthers & Strahan, 1923; Skelton, 1956). There are over a hundred smaller mines, trials and optimistic adits. The main ores were sulphides of lead, zinc and copper; small amounts of silver were obtained and traces of gold. Iron ore was mined at Stack Mooar and near Maughold Head in the northeast. The host rock for the veins was the Manx Group, particularly the Maughold Banded Formation, and the associated granites. Recorded production between 1845 and 1938 was 268,000 tons of lead concentrates, 256,000 tons of zinc concentrates, 14,000 tons of copper concentrates, 25,000 tons of iron ore and substantial amounts of silver, making the Manx mines some of the most productive in Britain. Foxdale ores were predominantly galena, mostly argentiferous, whilst at Laxey sphalerite was the chief ore. The Manx output amounted to a fifth of all the zinc ever produced in the British Isles, and perhaps as much as 5% of the lead. Small quantities of antimony, manganese, titanium, nickel and molybdenum ores have been found.

The success of the Manx mining industry in Victorian times has led the Manx Government into wishful thinking that it could be revived, and comprehensive surveys were commissioned in the 1950s to no avail. Indeed the widespread occurrence of mines and trials and the use of waste materials for roads and tracks throughout the island has led to so much contamination that stream-sediment geochemical surveys were of little value.

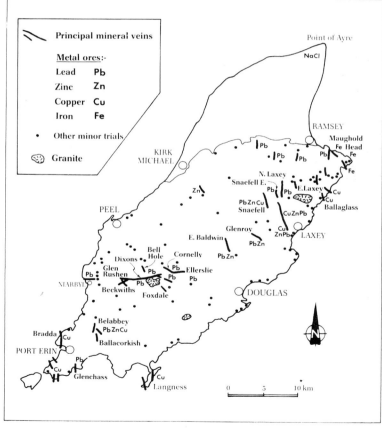

Figure 19: Sketch map of the mineral veins and mines of the Isle of Man.

Laxey

The lode at Laxey had a north-south trend and was inclined very steeply to the east. The lode was offset several times by "slides" or steeply inclined transverse faults and was eventually lost to the north in spite of extensive exploratory drivages. Mine trials in North Laxey Glen, some 2 km to the north, failed to find the same rich lode, but considerable quantities of lead and zinc ores were raised from a parallel lode at Snaefell Mine, some 3 km to the west. The deepest shaft at Laxey Mines reached 1812 feet (552m) below the main haulage adit, itself over 300 feet below the surface: the deepest workings were thus roughly 1100 feet (335m) below sea-level. Gangue minerals were mainly quartz, calcite and dolomite. Uranium-rich hydrocarbons have also been found. Apart from the elaborate pumping arrangements worked by the Laxey wheel (Figure 21), there was a water-pressure engine for man-riding (known as the man-engine), and a water-turbine used for haulage (Cowin & Scarffe, 1990). Mining stopped at Snaefell Mine in 1898 and at Great Laxey Mines in 1919 owing to a strike, but there were intermittent attempts to re-open the latter mine up to 1938. Shipping the concentrates out for smelting on the British mainland was a problem solved eventually by building a substantial quay at Laxey, just as the mines' yield was coming to an end! The waste heaps, particularly those at Snaefell, were re-processed for lead and copper in 1953-8.

Foxdale & Glen Rushen

The Foxdale and Glen Rushen Mines worked a major east-west lode some 5 km long with several parallel and branch veins as well as some short cross-courses (Figure 19). The mines at Foxdale itself were sunk directly into granite, but shafts such as Beckwith's Mine at Glen Rushen 2 km to the west (not to be confused with Beckwith's Shaft at Foxdale itself) were sunk into the Barrule Slates and reached granite at depth. Beckwith's Mine reached a depth of 2010 feet (613m), 1600 feet (488m) below sea-level. Granite was penetrated at a little over 100 m below surface. Lead ores predominated at Foxdale, though some rare copper-silver-antimony minerals were obtained at the slate-granite contact. Mining in the Foxdale - Glen Rushen area ceased in 1911.

Bradda Head

Immediately north of Port Erin bay, Bradda Head is transected by a strong north-south vein, clearly visible in the cliffs on both sides of the headland though access is not easy (Figure 20). On the south side a vertical rib of quartz up to 10 m wide is bordered by a breccia of slate and quartz. The ore was mainly copper sulphides and stimulated the

sinking of a shaft from the beach to more than 100 m below sea-level.
On the north side of the headland a complex of veins lies close to the
cliff and there are several openings to them. Much copper staining is
present on the cliff face. The quantities of ore raised at the Bradda
mines amount to 817 tons of copper concentrates and about 2000 tons
of lead concentrates, much less than at Foxdale or Laxey. Mining
ceased in 1883.

Minor quantities of lead, zinc and copper ores have been raised from
over 50 other mines, principally at Ballacorkish, Cornelly, Langness,
Dhoon, Glenchass, East Baldwin, Kirkmichael, Onchan, Douglas Head
and Bell Hole (north of Foxdale). As many more mine trials were made
elsewhere but failed to yield economic deposits. Haematite-quartz-
dolomite veins were worked for iron ore around Maughold Head from
adits driven into the cliffs from the Port e Vullen peninsula east of
Ramsey to Port Cornaa as well as from mines beneath Maughold
village (Hollis, 1987).

*Figure 20:
Bradda Head
seen from Port
Erin quay. The
mine chimney can
be seen on the
shore below the
tower, with the
cleft marking the
vein immediately
on its right
(locality II/3).*

Trevor D. Ford

Figure 21: The "Lady Isabella" or Great Laxey Wheel, erected in 1854 to pump the Laxey Mines dry (locality II/4).

The preliminary stages of ore processing were carried out on the island, and there were some early smelters but later on concentrates were shipped to Liverpool and Swansea for smelting. The processing yards at Foxdale have been re-used for other purposes since the mines closed or have become overgrown, but the remains of crushing floors and ore-washing buddles partly worked by a water-wheel and flat-rod system can be seen adjacent to Beckwith's Mine at Glen Rushen. A large part of the processing floors at Laxey have been built over or converted into gardens, but good samples of ore may be found amongst the cobbles on Laxey beach. Samples of the ores may be seen in the Manx Museum in Douglas.

The host rock for the mineral veins is the Manx Group or the intrusive granites though the ores are much younger: no veins of any significance have been found in the Carboniferous rocks, which might suggest a pre-Carboniferous age for mineralization, though there has also been some speculation that there was a cover of Carboniferous

Limestone at the time of mineralization. Ineson & Mitchell (1979) have determined K-Ar dates on some 30 clay gouges in veins or from altered wall-rocks. The dates indicates several episodes of mineralization at 310-320 Ma, 285 Ma, 250 Ma and 220 Ma with a possible Tertiary remobilization. These are mid- and late Carboniferous, Permian and Triassic, comparable with the dates obtained for similar mineral deposits in the Lake District. Mobilization of ore-fluids during periods of tectonic stress associated with the Armorican earth movements may have generated the ore deposits in the Isle of Man as in other parts of Britain.

SLATE

As noted above, much of the Manx "Slate" Group is not true slate, but one subdivision, the Barrule Slates, has been quarried for slate and is still quarried for building stone on South Barrule. Old "slate" quarries occur near Round Table, and in Glen Rushen. The three superimposed cleavages meant that the slates could not be split as thinly and evenly as those of North Wales and their use died out when bulk transport of the latter became possible. However, slabs for building walls could be obtained, and some of the South Barrule quarries are still yielding these. Flaggy beds of the Lonan Flags have similarly yielded building blocks, chiefly from the old quarries on Douglas Head.

BUILDING STONE

The flat-bedded massive sandstones in the Lonan and Niarbyl Flags have been quarried in various parts of the island, notably around Peel, where they were used for building the massive walls of Peel Castle. The red Peel Sandstone was quarried on Creg Malin headland north of Peel Bay. Good examples may be seen throughout Peel, particularly in the Cathedral. The Carboniferous Limestone was quarried, particularly from the foreshore, along the south coast. Three quarries near Ballasalla and Castletown are still producing limestone, mainly for aggregate and agricultural purposes.

SALT

Thick beds of halite were found in upper Triassic mudstones during the late 19th century by boring operations beneath the Point of Ayre and a brine-pumping industry started about the turn of the century. The brine was pumped through a pipe-line laid along the highwater mark of the beach below the Bride moraine to evaporation works at Ramsey; the pipe-line was breached by winter storms within a year or so and the salt industry soon came to an end.

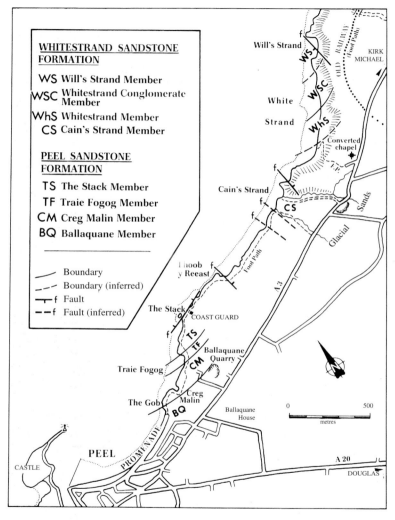

Figure 22: Sketch map of the Peel Sandstone Group (after Crowley, 1985).

PEEL SANDSTONES

About 2 km of the cliffs northeast of Peel have almost continuous outcrops of a sequence of red sandstones, conglomerates, mudstones and calcareous "cornstones" (calcretes) (Figure 22). The last represent

Figure 23: The Peel Sandstone section in Traie Fogog Bay, north of Peel (locality III/1).

Figure 24: Calcrete (= cornstone) horizon in the Peel Sandstone, White Strand Bay (locality III/2).

ancient soils (palaeosols) with much concretionary calcite (Figure 24). The beds dip northwest, i.e.seawards, at angles between 15 and 50 degrees (Figure 23). The only exposed contact with surrounding rocks is a fault against slates of the Manx Group with a dolerite intrusion in Wills Strand Bay. The southern contact with the Manx Group is probably also faulted but this is entirely concealed by Peel town and harbour. Elsewhere the Peel sandstones (now Peel Group according to the Rules of Stratigraphic Nomenclature) are covered by Pleistocene drift. No indigenous fossils have been recorded though derived fossils in pebbles are well known and are discussed below. Devonian (lower or upper), Carboniferous, Permian and Triassic ages have been proposed, but the most cogently expressed argument is that of Allen & Crowley (1983) who favour a lower Devonian (Old Red Sandstone) age, on both sedimentological and structural grounds. Boyd Dawkins (1902) thought that the sequence was about 500m thick, repeated by faulting, but recent studies have shown that the lithofacies, not the beds themselves, is repeated and that the total observed thickness is about 1000 m. Perhaps another 500 m can be inferred beneath the drift cover. In a brief outline of the Peel Group, Crowley (1985) has listed a sequence of two formations consisting of eight members, though no full description has been published and there are some gaps due to faulting. The following is taken from his work with minor modifications (the letters refer to outcrops on Figure 22):

Whitestrand Sandstone Formation:

8. Will's Strand Member (WS) - sandstone-dominated low sinuosity alluvial beds with spectacular deformation.
7. Whitestrand Conglomerate Member (WSC) - distal alluvial fan conglomerates and pebbly sandstones.
6. Whitestrand Member (W) - distal alluvial fan sandstones and siltstones, some conglomerates,abundant desiccation structures, sparse calcrete.
5. Cain's Strand Member (CS)- sandstone-dominated low sinuosity fluvial facies.

Peel Sandstone Formation:

4. The Stack Member (TS) - medial alluvial fan conglomerates, pebbly sandstones and sandstones with abundant calcretes.
3. Traie Fogog Member (TF) - distal to medial alluvial fan conglomerates, sandstones, siltstones and mudstones; abundant desiccation features and sparse calcretes.
2. Creg Malin Member (CM)-stacked fining-upwards cycles -active low sinuosity streams.
1. Ballaquane Member (Bq)-conglomerate and sandstone-dominated low sinuosity channels; sheet-flood sandstones.

The overall sedimentation pattern is of coalescing, low sinuosity alluvial fans and alluvial plains of typical Old Red Sandstone style. Current directions and slump structures indicate a source northwest of the Isle of Man, i.e. with rivers flowing towards a much lower Manx massif. Indeed, if the Peel sandstones are restored to horizontality and projected inland they would pass right over the present day Manx slate massif. Strong slump folding (Figure 25) and thrusting (Figure 26) seen at the north end of White Strand Bay suggest contemporaneous tectonic disturbance of the alluvial fans with movement southeastwards towards the Isle of Man (Ford, 1972). The angularity of pebbles and their composition including limestones suggests that the source was not more than 5-10 km away. Furthermore, pebbles in the Stack Member have yielded a variety of derived Wenlock limestone fossils, whilst pebbles in the Whitestrand Conglomerate Member have yielded Ashgillian fossils. Together with a variety of acid igneous pebbles this "inverted clast stratigraphy" suggests that an area of upper Ordovician to middle Silurian shelf sediments and volcanics lay not far northwest of the Isle of Man, and was progressively eroded during Devonian times. The deformation of the Peel Sandstones appears to have taken place during Middle to early Upper Devonian times, indicating that sedimentation was in Lower Devonian times, probably not long after the Caledonian folding of the Manx Group and the emplacement of the Manx granites. Taken with the scattered outcrops of Old Red Sandstone in Anglesey, northeast Ireland, southern Scotland and the Lake District the Peel sandstones suggest that there was a widespread alluvial fan and plain over much of the Irish Sea area, though little evidence of it has yet been found in sea-floor exploration.

Figure 25: Slump fold in the Peel Sandstones, north end of White Strand Bay (locality III/2).

Fig 26: Slump thrusts, Peel Sandstones, north end of White Strand Bay (locality III/2).

THE CARBONIFEROUS LIMESTONE

Some 10 km of the south coast has almost continuous outcrops of
Carboniferous Limestone with associated volcanics either side of
Castletown, with a faulted outlier at Port St Mary (Figure 27). There is
a wide variety of lithofacies, with locally abundant fossil faunas (good
collections are in the Manx Museum in Douglas, and lists may be found
in Lamplugh, 1903; Lewis, 1930; Dickson, *et al.* 1987). A combination
of mapping and palaeontology has enabled a stratigraphic sequence to
be established, though faults break up continuous sections. The
sequence of formations and members, with approximate stage
assignations is as follows (after Dickson, *et al.*, 1987):-

Scarlett Volcanic Formation	50 m+ ⎱	
Close-ny-Chollagh Formation	57 m ⎰	Brigantian
Poyllvaaish Formation	78 m ⎱	
Balladoole Formation	90 m ⎰	Asbian
Castletown Formation		
Scarlett Point Member	14 m ⎫	
Sea Mount Member	6 m ⎬	Holkerian
Knockrushen Member	21 m ⎭	
Derbyhaven (& Ballasalla) Formation		
Skillicore Member	21 m ⎫	
Ronaldsway Member	22 m ⎬	Arundian
Sandwick Member	24 m	
Turkeyland Member	18 m ⎭	
Langness Conglomerate	30 m	Chadian ?
Total	431 m	

The Isle of Man

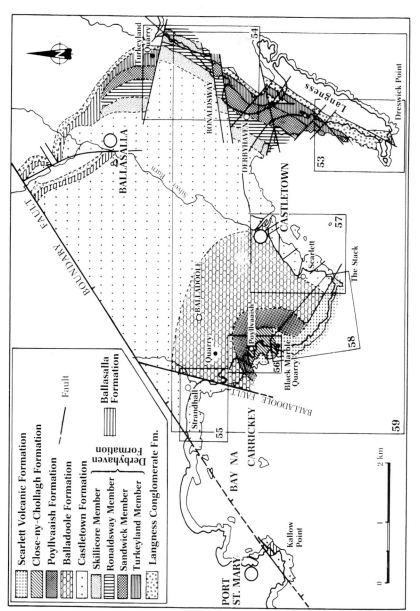

Figure 27: Sketch map of the geology of the Carboniferous Limestone around Castletown (after Dickson et al. 1987).

Trevor D. Ford

Figure 28: Langness Conglomerate resting unconformably on Lonan Flags, Dreswick Harbour, Langness (locality IV/1).

Figure 29: Mega-ripples in the Derbyhaven Formation; close to the light gantry on the foreshore east of Ronaldsway airport (locality IV/2).

Figure 30: Monoclinal fold in limestones of the Castletown Formation Scarlett Point (locality IV/6).

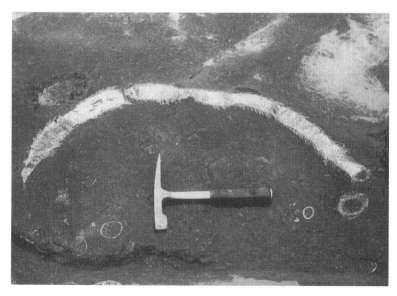

Figure 31: The World's largest Caninid coral? Strandhall shore (locality IV/4).

Figure 32: Hummocky Ballasalla (= Castletown) limestones at Kallow Point, Port St Mary (locality IV/3).

Figure 33: Crowded Zaphrentid corals at Kallow Point, Port St Mary (locality IV/3).

Figure 34: The higher black shaly beds of the Close-ny-Chollagh Formation, Black Marble Quarry (locality IV/5).

Figure 35: Deeply corroded foundered limestone block (right centre) with off-lapping beds of the Close-ny-Chollagh Formation. Build-ups of the Poyllvaaish Formation are seen in the background across Ghaw Gortagh inlet (locality IV/5).

Trevor D. Ford

Figure 36: Contorted black beds beneath a foundered limestone build-up, by Poyllvaaish Farm (locality IV/5) (photo by D. G. Quirk).

Figure 37: Coarse basaltic agglomerate, Scarlett Volcanics (locality V/7).

Figure 38: Pillow lavas, southeast of Close-ny-Chollagh Point (locality V/2).

The LANGNESS CONGLOMERATE is exposed on the west coast of the Langness Peninsula, where it makes impressive scenery of arches and gullies (Figure 28). It is composed of derived clasts of the Lonan Flags division of the Manx Group, and rests unconformably on steeply dipping or even overturned beds thereof. On the tip of the peninsula, near the lighthouse, the topmost slates are stained red and show a very uneven palaeo-topography. The poor sorting and irregular shape of the clasts, together with lenses of sandstone and mud-flake breccia, suggest deposition from sheet floods on an alluvial fan. The Conglomerate passes up into limestones without a break.

The DERBYHAVEN FORMATION is exposed on the foreshore from Langness northeastwards across Derbyhaven Bay and beneath Ronaldsway airport as far as the bounding fault at Cass-ny-Hawin. It consists generally of thin dark limestones with shale partings, and contains scattered corals. Some beds are markedly lenticular, and others have mega-ripples on their surfaces (Figure 29); a few have scattered quartz pebbles. Sections are available immediately inland at Turkeyland quarries, and at Ballasalla quarries, though the latter cannot be correlated directly with the shore sections. The Derbyhaven Formation has been subdivided into four members on the basis of subtle changes in average grain size, bed thickness and thickness of shale partings.

The CASTLETOWN FORMATION is exposed in much-faulted outcrops from Castletown as far as Scarlett Point. It is mostly composed of thin, rather dark beds, but with individual beds packed with corals (large *Siphonophyllia*), large brachiopods (*Megachonetes*), bryozoa, goniatites (*Merocanites*) and some dolomitized beds. On Scarlett Point itself there is a group of well-exposed folds (Figure 30). The formation re-appears with scattered large solitary corals (*Siphonophyllia*, Figure 31) at Strandhall to the west before being cut off by a fault, and there is an interesting outlier at Kallow Point at Port St Mary, with numerous corals, bryozoa, *Zoophycos* trails and scattered quartz pebbles; one bed is notable for its hummocky surface due to incipient nodule formation (Figures 32 & 33). The Castletown Formation has been subdivided into three members on the basis of bed thickness, presence of distinctive fossils, dolomitic beds and chert.

The BALLADOOLE FORMATION is exposed though much dolomitized and fractured on the foreshore from Poyll Ritchie to Salt Spring. The Balladoole and Cross Welkin (= Fisher Hill) quarries show the formation to be calcite mudstones often developing weakly fossiliferous mud mound build-ups. The Balladoole Formation re-appears briefly beneath the dolomitized Poyllvaaish Formation at low tide mark at Scarlett Point.

The POYLLVAAISH FORMATION forms a small headland between Salt Spring and the Ghaw Gortagh inlet northwest of Poyllvaaish Farm. The formation is composed of massive, light-coloured,shelly calcite mudstones, very largely in the form of heaped build-ups (formerly known as "reefs" or mud-mounds). Most of the Poyllvaaish Formation is highly fossiliferous, and one bed is packed with goniatites, particularly *Goniatites crenistria* and *Beyrichoceratoides truncatum*. A small patch of Poyllvaaish Formation appears, somewhat brecciated and dolomitized, faulted against the volcanics at Scarlett Point. The Poyllvaaish Formation dips beneath the thin black limestones and boulder-beds of the Close-ny-Chollagh Formation in the Ghaw Gortagh inlet adjacent to Poyllvaaish Farm.

The CLOSE-NY-CHOLLAGH FORMATION occupies the foreshore from Ghaw Gortagh inlet past Poyllvaaish Farm as far as the base of the volcanics at Close-ny-Chollagh Point. Whilst much of the formation is thin black limestones or shales, as seen in the Black Marble quarry (Figure 34), the lower part is a jumble of large foundered blocks, breccia beds, and density flow beds interlayered with variously undisturbed or contorted black beds (Figures 35 & 36). These are thought to be due to the collapse of a spread of build-ups over unconsolidated muds adjacent to a syn-sedimentary fault (Quirk, *et al*, 1990).

Figure 39: Part of the "Great Wall" of basalt emplaced in coarse agglomerate, Scarlett volcanics (locality V/7).

Figure 40: One of three olivine dolerite dykes by Poyllvaaish Farm, looking across Ghaw Gortagh inlet. (locality VI/3). (photo D. G. Quirk).

The SCARLETT VOLCANIC FORMATION outcrops along the coast for 1500 m from Close-ny-Chollagh Point to Scarlett Point. It is composed of a pile of basaltic agglomerates, ashes and lavas with many different varieties of volcanic outpourings and their relationships well exposed (Figures 37 & 38). Dykes of basalt cut the agglomerates forming wall-like masses, one with ropy surfaces on both sides (Figure 39). One section of lavas shows good pillows (Figure 38); another, in The Stack itself, shows columnar structure; other lavas are either massive or highly vesicular. One section of coarse agglomerate is made almost entirely of vesicular basalt blocks; slumped breccias of lavas and ashes sometimes contain limestone blocks. Several lenses of black limestone are interleaved with agglomerates, indicating that at least some of the eruptions were on to the sea floor. Dykes of both Carboniferous and post-Carboniferous (Tertiary) age occur cutting the agglomerates.

The Scarlett Volcanics are the youngest Carboniferous beds visible on the Isle of Man, though lower Namurian (Yoredale) beds are known to be present beneath the Pleistocene drift of the north end of the Isle.

The relationship of the Lower Carboniferous sequence to the Manx Group massif is uncertain. Apart from the unconformity on Langness, the boundaries of the limestone area are entirely faults. Nowhere are lateral changes in the lithofacies sufficiently well-developed to indicate the position or direction of a shoreline, though the presence of scattered quartz pebbles suggests that it was not far away. The probable environment of deposition was a shallow shelf adjacent to the Manx massif. The foundered limestone blocks of the Close-ny-Chollagh Formation suggest that this shelf was tectonically unstable. The nature of the volcanics hints at the presence of a volcanic centre just offshore, perhaps close to The Stack of Scarlett itself.

The Dinantian limestone sequence of the Castletown area has some similarities to that seen in Furness and the Pennine basin, but it is in marked contrast to the 600m sequence of limestones, shales, sandstones and thin coals penetrated in boreholes through the drift of the northern plain of the Isle of Man. The sequence here has closer similarities to the Dinantian of Cumbria. The contrast between the limestone sequences in the north and south of the Island has been taken to support the concept of a Manx massif between them in Dinantian times. Lower Namurian strata have also been proved in the northern boreholes, but the optimistic search for Coal Measures has failed so far.

TERTIARY DYKES

Many olivine dolerite dykes cut the rocks of the Isle of Man. Lamplugh (1903) listed some 80 of them. Whilst they occur on most of the coastal sections and in a scatter of stream-bottom exposures inland, they are most accessible cutting the Carboniferous Limestone on the foreshores either side of Castletown. Most of the dykes have a general northwest to southeast trend and may be related to the igneous complexes of Northern Ireland, though their orientation is well to the north of the Mourne Mountains. Individual dykes are up to 6 metres wide, and often show bands of amygdules parallel to their sides. Chilled margins are less obvious and contact alteration of the enclosing country rock is rarely more than 2 or 3 centimetres wide. Dykes which split and rejoin are common. A few dykes can be seen to cut the Langness Conglomerate, and one changes its direction of hade on passing from conglomerate down into the Manx Group.

No detailed research is known to have been done on the petrology or geochemistry of the dykes, and the only isotope-dating is on associated fault gouges (Ineson & Mitchell, 1979) who deduced an average age of about 50 million years.

Good examples of the dykes are to be found on the foreshore at Strandhall, around Poyllvaaish (Figure 40), Scarlett Point, Castletown Bay, the Ronaldsway shore and Langness. A few dykes cut the Scarlett Volcanic Formation and, whilst both are basaltic, the Tertiary dykes are so much fresher in appearance that they are unmistakeable.

THE QUATERNARY OF THE ISLE OF MAN

Almost a third of the Isle of Man, north of the mountain front between Kirkmichael and Ramsey, is composed of Pleistocene glacial and associated deposits (Figures 41 & 42) . The northwestern and northeastern coasts provide almost continuous sections of these deposits, rivalling only the Pleistocene sections of the Norfolk Coast. Totalling some 25 km the cliffs provide highly instructive examples of the relationships of tills, moraines, outwash fans, lake deposits, kettle holes, spillway channels, and post-glacial features (Figure 43). At the same time the drift deposits present several problems of interpretation (see Thomas, 1976, 1977; Eyles & Eyles, 1984; and Dackombe & Thomas, 1985).

The Isle of Man's position in the northern Irish Sea places it directly in line of the advance of Scottish ice sheets, constrained laterally by Lake District and Northern Irish ice. There is little doubt that the island was overrun by Scottish ice more than once, but the pre-Devensian glaciations and interglacials are known only from deposits encountered in boreholes below sea-level under the northern plain, and no accurate dates are available for them. A bevelled surface sloping from -40 m north of the mountain front to below -125 m beneath the Point of Ayre trims solid formations ranging from the Manx Group, through Carboniferous Limestones, Yoredales, and Permian (?) to Triassic. The

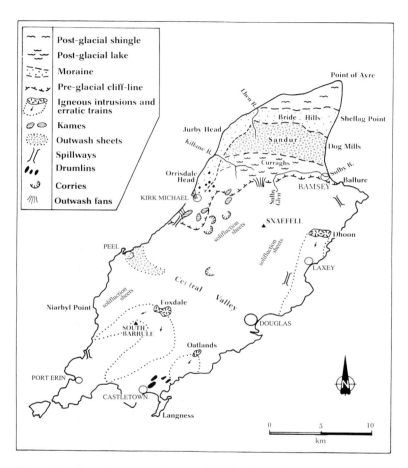

Figure 41: Sketch map of Pleistocene glacial and associated features of the Isle of Man (after Thomas, 1976 & 1977).

coastal sections are all in Devensian or post-glacial deposits; in fact they are mostly late Devensian. Thomas (1976) has proposed a stratigraphic nomenclature of some 50 formational names owing to the problems of correlation from one part of the coastal cliffs to another, and to the upland exposures to the south. In the interests of simplicity only those names relating to sections described in the Itineraries are given herein. Holocene deposits lie to the north of the moraines and are best seen in The Ayres (Figure 44).

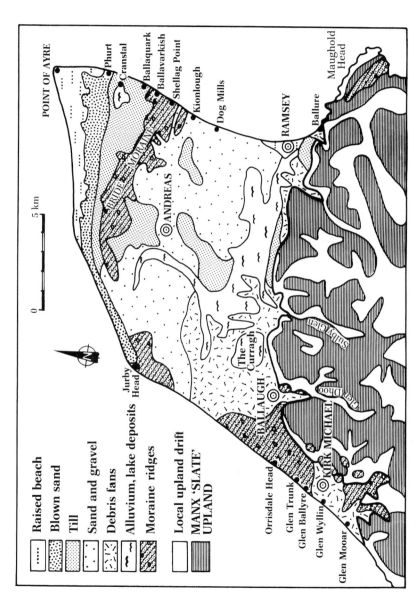

Figure 42: Sketch map of Pleistocene geology of the northern plain (after Thomas, 1977).

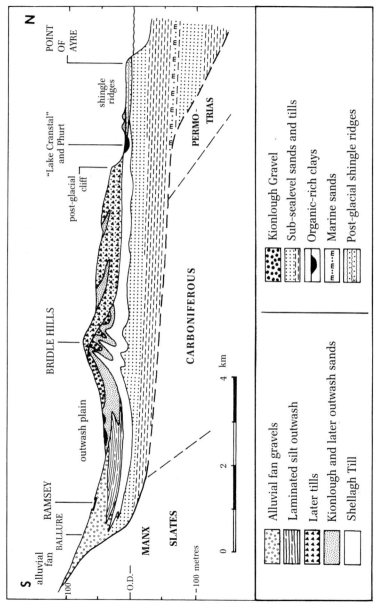

Figure 43: Diagrammatic section to show the relationships of glacial deposits at the northern end of the Isle of Man (after Robinson & McCarroll, 1990).

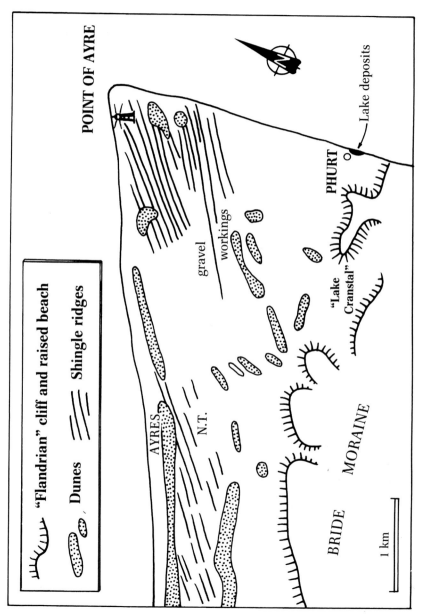

Figure 44: Sketch map of the Holocene sand and gravel area of the Point of Ayre (after Thomas, QRA guide).

The Manx uplands are largely devoid of classic glacial features such as corries and U-shaped valleys, the upper part of Laxey Glen alone approximating to a glacial trough. Most of the valleys are mantled with a thick cover of drift. Present day stream courses are deeply incised into the drift, and there is a blanket of peat on higher ground. The drift is locally derived material from the Manx Group in contrast to the coastal drift which is very largely externally derived from the west of Scotland and the northern Irish Sea floor. Some of the upland slaty drift has been interpreted as boulder clay but it has been reworked by solifluction processes. In a few sections different sheets of soliflucted material can be distinguished by colour or by the amount of clay matrix. No direct evidence of the age of these deposits is available and it is generally assumed that they are Devensian. The solifluction deposits mantle all but the highest peaks suggesting that they might have been nunataks projecting through the ice probably in late Devensian times. Even the highest peak, Snaefell, is much lower than the summits of the Lake District where glacial features are much more pronounced.

Erratic trains derived from the granites generally lie upon the slaty drift to the south of the three intrusions; granite erratics have been found as much as 280 m above the highest bedrock source, demonstrating the power and thickness of the over-riding ice. Small patches of till, with striated pavements beneath them in some cases, occur on the southern coasts, e.g. at Port St Mary.

Figure 45: Orrisdale Sands and Gravels overlying Orrisdale Till; Orrisdale Head (locality VII/3).

Figure 46: Inverted-L-shaped intrusion of Carboniferous Limestone blocks in till at Jurby Head (outline drawn in) (locality VII/5).

The Manx Group upland was breached in two places by over-riding glaciers, at Fleshwick near Port Erin, and the central valley from Peel and Douglas. The latter has extensive outwash sand and gravel fans, quarried for aggregate near St Johns. Raised beach deposits are present along parts of the western and southern coasts; a good example is at Calf Sound, at the southern tip of the Isle. Drainage of the northern uplands has given rise to delta fans of slaty debris, which overlie the external drift as around Kirkmichael or lie upon the distal end of the outwash plains as at the mouth of Sulby Glen and around Ballaugh. Kames where detritus spilled into pro-glacial lakes are prominent features near Kirkmichael and Ballaugh.

The drift plain of the north is dominated by the Bride moraine rising to about 100 m above sea-level at Shellag Point but less well-defined where the cliffs between Orrisdale and Jurby Heads provide an oblique section (Figures 45 & 46). The Bride moraine is a striking terminal push-moraine resulting from a late Devensian re-advance over earlier Devensian till sheets. The ice-sheet had a "snow-plough effect" on previous deposits and Shellag Point shows unrivalled sections of glacio-

Figure 47: Thrust and folded tills and gravel sheets of the Bride moraine at Shellag Point (locality VIII/4).

Figure 48: Contorted Kionlough Sands and Gravels, covered by overthrust till, Shellag Point (locality VIII/4).

Figure 49: Load structures in outwash silts and clays, Dog Mills (locality VIII/3).

tectonics, where tills, sands and gravels are isoclinally folded and have several thrust faults (Figures 47 & 48). In turn they are overlain discordantly by undisturbed later till and outwash. Immediately to the south is a complex of tills and a sandur or outwash plain passing into pro-glacial lake deposits, seen in the cliffs north of Ramsey (Figure 49). In the 19th century a scatter of small brickworks utilized the more clay-rich tills or outwash sediments at several points around the island, and that at Ballacorey (433988) continued production up to 1925, though the high calcium carbonate content resulted in rather poor quality bricks. Some of the outwash silts contain fossil foraminifera suggesting a marine embayment near Dog Mills. On the south side of the Bride moraine there is a complex of dry valleys draining southwards, once the spillways for melt-water streams from the ice margin. Cross-sections of several kettle holes are to be seen in the cliffs near Kirkmichael (Figure 50). The pro-glacial Curragh lake was eventually filled with peaty muds in post-glacial times leaving an area of fertile if swampy soils drained by streams which breached the western moraines at The Lhen and the Killane River, whilst the Sulby Glen river turned eastwards towards Ramsey. Patches of the Curragh swamps can be seen within the Wildlife Park, west of Sulby.

Trevor D. Ford

There is some debate as to whether the ice ploughing up the Bride moraine was terrestrial, resting on land exposed by the lower Devensian sea-level, or whether it was floating sea-ice. The evidence is at least partly capable of interpretation for either process but the sea-ice hypothesis would require sea-level to have been much higher than the present at a time when the evidence from the rest of Britain suggests that it was much lower (Eyles & Eyles, 1984; Dackombe & Thomas., 1985). The sea-ice hypothesis would also make the explanation of some features such as kettle holes, kame terraces, and the presence of the Great Irish Deer rather difficult.

The lowest visible deposits of the northwest coast sections include sands with numerous marine shells such as *Turritella*, presumably derived by the ice scraping them up from the floor of the northern Irish Sea. Some of the shells are delicate and indicative of a more temperate climate so that it is difficult to see how they could have survived transport unless frozen into a block of ice-impregnated sand.

The Bride moraine around Jurby and Kirkmichael is more subdued than at Bride and shows topographic features characteristic of ice-wastage. The cliffs around Orrisdale Head (Figure 45) show magnificent sections through outwash gravels, sands and silts (Thomas, et al. 1985). On top of these are sections through several infilled kettle holes (Figure 50): layers of peat with a rich fossil flora, marls with *Chara* and a fauna of various Coleoptera have yielded anomalously early radio-carbon dates of around 18000BP from their basal deposits, whilst a silt only 30 cm higher has yielded a date of 12150 years BP; the latter indicates that glacial retreat must have cleared the Isle of Man at the latest by 12000 years ago. The youngest kettle hole deposits are around 10000 years old, with implications for the date of final deglaciation of other parts of the Irish Sea basin (Thomas, 1977; Dackombe & Thomas, 1985). The kettle holes have yielded several fine specimens of the Giant Irish Deer *Megaloceras*. Some hollows near Ballaugh have been interpreted as pingoes, due to growth of peri-glacial ice masses; the resultant hollows persisted into post-glacial times. Parts of the northwest cliffs are capped by extensive debris fans of local material washed out from the uplands. In turn these are covered by wind-blown sand; cryoturbation features are locally common in the upper layers of these sections.

The upstream side of the Bride moraine was trimmed by the post-glacial rise in sea-level, and a low Flandrian cliff faces north across the Ayres gravel plain with its numerous storm ridges, slacks and dunes extending to the Point of Ayre (Ward, 1970; Tooley, 1978) (Figure 44). Here, a massive shingle bank has formed from pebbles derived partly from glacial deposits on the floor of the Irish Sea and partly from

Figure 50: Kettle hole deposits at Glen Wyllin. Note thick Chara marl at the base (locality VII/2).

northward long-shore drift from the eroding glacial deposits on the coasts; now well-rounded, these pebbles include many samples of riebeckite-microgranite from the island of Ailsa Craig off the Ayrshire coast demonstrating that this small intrusion must have been much larger at one time, and has been reduced by ice action. There are also many flint pebbles which provided the Mesolithic and Neolithic peoples with material for implements. The post-glacial Lake Cranstal was dammed up between the north face of the Bride moraine and the pebble ridges, and sections of related deposits occur in the cliff at Phurt. A Flandrian raised beach and fossil cliff line are also present just north of Ramsey, where the distal end of the sandur was trimmed during a high post-glacial sea-level.

The unconsolidated nature of the Pleistocene sediments on the northwest and northeast coasts makes them particularly liable to marine erosion and rates of cliff retreat of as much as one metre per annum have been noted. The detritus drifts northwards to the Point of Ayre. The cliff erosion also means that the details of what is visible change after every storm.

Landslips occur in the hard rocks of the eastern and southern coasts: south of Douglas parts of the Marine Drive have collapsed reducing the road to a narrow footpath. At the Chasms on the south side of Meall Hill, a large slice of quartzites within the Maughold Banded Pelites is in suspended animation having moved outwards opening deep clefts by as much as two metres.

Trevor D. Ford

ITINERARIES

With the Isle of Man being a small island, and assuming that transport is by car or minibus, the itineraries are arranged by stratigraphic unit. Visiting geologists with little time available may find it useful to extract a few localities from each itinerary and make up stratigraphically mixed routes of their own. Coaches can be hired on the island or brought over by ferry, but the narrow lanes leading to many of the coastal localities make it easier to organize excursions by minibus rather than coach, and it is recommended that parties be kept to less than 20.

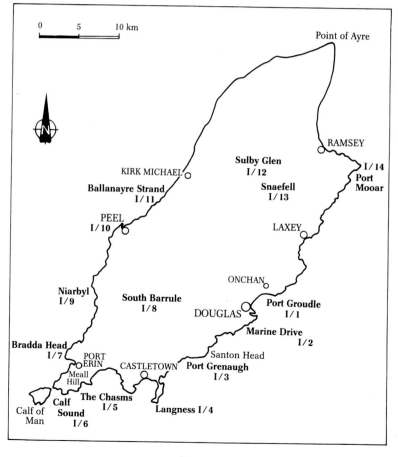

Figure 51: Localities for Itinerary I - the Manx Group.

The 1:50000 Ordnance Survey map sheet 95 covers the whole island, and there is a reprint edition of Lamplugh's Geological Survey Special Isle of Man sheet available (comprising parts of Sheets 36, 46, 47, 56 & 57). National Grid References are in 100 km square SC except for the extreme north (all Quaternary deposits) which is in square NX.

Permission to visit localities other than beaches and shore exposures is usually freely given, but party leaders should plan their itineraries and write for appropriate permission beforehand. For the Foxdale, Poortown and Barrule Beg quarries write to the Quarry Manager, Mr. S. Taylor, at Poortown, Peel. Most disused quarries are now in the care of the Manx Government's Department of Industry (c/o Mr. L. Crellin, Illiam Dhone House, 2 Circular Road, Douglas), from whom permission should be sought. Localities on foreshores mostly necessitate keeping a careful eye on tides, and it is wise to consult tide tables beforehand.

I MANX GROUP

The object of this itinerary is to demonstrate as many of the different lithologies, fold styles and metamorphic grades of the various subdivisions of the Manx Group as is practicable. The recommended localities are spread round the east, south and west coasts and a route planned thus will cover most of the important features of the Manx Group (Figure 51).

Locality I/1. Port Groudle, Onchan. Drive down the narrow lane off the coastal road north from Douglas (A11) to a car park at 420784 (the lane is not suitable for coaches). Walk to the bay (Port is Manx for Bay) at 421782 and take the rough path round the southern headland. The Lonan Flags here have dips ranging from 65° to near vertical on the southeast limb of the F1 Douglas syncline and young inland. They can be examined in detail adjacent to the path and there are good views of the structures in the cliffs to the north (Figure 9). After some 300 m at 420780 a hornblende-rich lamprophyre dyke some 12 m thick and inclined at about 30° to the south cuts the flags; xenoliths, vein quartz blebs and vesicles occur along the margins. Return to the vehicles.

Locality I/2. Marine Drive, Douglas. (Roadside parking suitable for minibuses but coaches should not be taken south of Douglas Head). Leaving Douglas by the Marine Drive over Douglas Head, the road should be followed for about 1 km to a bend where vertical beds stand at the right-hand (west) roadside directly opposite a small car park (381742); these have worm-track trace fossils up to 1 cm wide and 25 cm long on several sole surfaces. Continue for 1.5 km to the barrier beyond which there is pedestrian access only. At the first embayment,

Walberry Hill (371735), the Lonan Flags may be seen both above and below the defunct road with the strata nearly vertical and younging inland towards the axis of the Douglas Head syncline (Figure 10). The beds are greywackes around 10-20 cm in thickness alternating with similar thicknesses of pelite. Graded bedding is present in some couplets. About 1.5 km further southwest at The Whing embayment (360733) similar beds may be seen with rather more pelite, and with the inland dip somewhat reduced. The seaward dip of S1 cleavage confirms that the fold axis lies inland. At both localities the coarser beds have much quartz veining in joints. Either return to the transport near Walberry Hill, or continue for 1 km to the second barrier at Kerristal (352732) to rejoin the transport if drivers can be sent round. Drive to Port Grenaugh.

Locality I/3. Port Grenaugh to Santon Head. (Roadside parking at Port Grenaugh (316705) is suitable for minibuses). Two short walks can be made here, one southwest and the other northeast. Taking the southwestern path first along the cliff-top path round the southern headland, a thin-bedded pelitic facies of the Lonan Flags has a steep dip (70-80°) inland on the northwest flank of the Dhoon anticline. The Flags can also be seen to be cut by many pre-F1 basic dykes, mostly chloritized and often deformed by F1 shearing. F1 cross-folding is present plunging steeply south parallel to S1 axial planar cleavage. Traces of low angle S2 cleavage are visible in places. These structures are well displayed in an inlet some 400 m to the south accessible down a rough scramble down a gulley (313702). A Tertiary olivine dolerite dyke is also present in this inlet (mid to low tide recommended).

Return to the road at Port Grenaugh and take the cliff-top path to the northeast. After a few hundred metres there is an archaeological site, Cronk ny Merriu, consisting of an Early Iron Age promontory fort with an early Christian Keill (=chapel) within it (318704). Continue for 1.5 km to the east. The cliffs are mainly pelite-rich greywackes of the Lonan Flags with 45° dips seawards as the axis of the Douglas Head syncline has been faulted seawards. Greenstone dykes are common though few are visible from the cliff-top path. At the first bay, Purt Veg, (326703) descend to the shore (moderately low tide necessary) and traverse out to Baltic Rock headland beyond examining a series of massive arenaceous greywackes dipping at around 20° southeast; climb on to the headland which is on the axis of a syncline plunging gently northeast. Rippled surfaces are common here, and micaceous siltstones have recently yielded Didymograptid graptolites of probable Arenigian age. Santon Head lies 0.5 km to the east, with the beds folded on the axis of the Douglas Head syncline. Return to Port Grenaugh.

Locality I/4. Langness. From Castletown drive to Derbyhaven; turn right and shortly right again by a ruined building, a former smelter and ore-house, and immediately left across the golf course to the car park on the site of the Langness Mine (284659) (suitable for minibuses). Walk to the lighthouse (283652) and turn left (east) on nearly vertical pelitic Lonan Flags. Continue northwards on the east coast of the peninsula crossing Lonan Flags overturned as shown by graded bedding, rare current bedding, ripple-marks, scour-channels and trace-fossils. There are numerous greenstone dykes, though most have weathered back and are concealed beneath turf or seaweed in gullies (locally called gullets!). On reaching the golf course turn back across the peninsula to rejoin the road and car park.

Drive via Castletown and Port St Mary to Meall Hill and Cregneish village.

Locality I/5. Meall Hill & The Chasms. The car park adjacent to the old Manx village of Cregneish (191 674) is in an old quarry and provides an easily accessible section in quartzitic sandstones within the Maughold Banded Pelites, here dipping at about 35° to the south-southeast. The bedding is crossed by small F2 folds plunging east-northeast with an S2 cleavage (Figure 12). Strong S3 axial plane cleavage dips east-northeast. The summit of Meall Hill, reached by a track from the village, has an unusual archaeological site of six Neolithic tombs arranged in a circle. From the main road, turn left in the village and drive about a kilometre to the south to a rough car park by a radio building (191665), whence a path leads down to The Chasms (192663), a landslip in suspended animation developed in a second quartzitic sandstone in the Maughold Banded Pelites. The beds here have a gentle seaward dip on the northern limb of the Spanish Head syncline. They are split into large blocks by joints up to 2 m wide on both strike and dip directions.

Return to the vehicles and drive via Cregneish to Calf Sound.

Locality I/6. Calf Sound. (Ample car and bus parking - possible charge). At this southwestern tip of the Isle of Man (173667) the cliffs and shore are in the Maughold Banded Pelites showing rapid alternations of pelite and siltstone, here more or less vertical and younging to the southeast (Figure 13). The cafe and car park are on a raised beach and sections showing cryoturbation occur near the cliff edge. There are good views of the tide race in the channel with the Calf of Man island beyond; roughly 2.6 square kilometres in area the Calf is a bird sanctuary and is entirely in the Maughold Banded Pelites of the Manx Group: it can be visited by boat from Port Erin during the summer months. About 1 km to the southeast the western face of Spanish Head shows a section across the synclinal axis of an F1 fold, and there is an inaccessible dolerite intrusion in the cliffs; large slabs of fine-grained greywacke were quarried here for use as lintels and flooring, e.g. at Rushen Castle in Castletown. Drive to Bradda Head.

Locality I/7. Bradda Head. At the extreme north end of the front at Port Erin, a narrow lane behind the houses of Bradda West Road leads to a small car park at 192697, suitable for minibuses. From here a footpath leads west along the contour towards Bradda Head; where it starts to climb the Head there are views of the South Bradda Mine chimney on a rocky beach (Figure 20): the cliff above is in contorted pelites with much quartz veining in the Maughold Banded Pelites (Figure 17). From the Tower on the top there are views of the northwest side of the headland and of the coast beyond. A walk northwards along the cliff top to 187707 reveals the sharp contact of the Barrule Slates and the Maughold Banded Pelites. Return to the car park and drive north towards Peel via the A36 road. At the summit, about 231747, a path leads west on to Cronk ny Arrey Loo where there are some small quarries in the Barrule Slates. A southward traverse along the heather-covered ridge crosses several porphyrite sheets whose light colour contrasts with the dark slates. Returning to the road a stop about 1 km further on, at Cronk Fedjag (240750) provides a viewpoint from which the fundamental structure of the F1 Manx syncline may be seen. Here, we are on the Barrule Slate outcrop on the southeastern limb, whilst about 1.5 to 2 km to the north a series of quarries in the same formation are visible in Glen Rushen on the northwestern limb. The intervening low ground is occupied by the Injebreck Banded Pelites in the core of the syncline. Some of the Glen Rushen mines, visible in the distance, start in this formation. Continuing to the crossroads known as Round Table (246758) a footpath to the summit of South Barrule starts about 100 m down the Castletown road. Note many vein quartz blocks on the moors and in walls around here in the metamorphic axis of the Island.

Locality I/8. South Barrule. Continue northeast from Round Table round the north flank of South Barrule. (Note the Glen Rushen mine buildings on the left - see Itinerary II). Whilst there are several small quarries in the Barrule Slates near this road, the slates are best seen in the working Barrule Beg quarry at the northeast end of the hill at 270770 (permission from Mr. S. Taylor, the Manager of Poortown Quarry, Peel). Drive up the rough track to the quarry. The S2 cleavage is nearly horizontal here giving a spurious flat-bedded appearance to the quarry face. Bedding is obscure and the subtle changes of grain-size are difficult to find. Bedding/cleavage relationships show better in loose slabs. A good view over Foxdale village and its mining relics is to be had from the road below the quarry approach. Return to Round Table and turn right (west) on the coast road (A27) towards Peel, turning down to the shore at Dalby to reach Niarbyl Point.

Locality I/9. Niarbyl Point. Either park by the cafe on top of the headland or if space permits take cars down to the point: low to mid tide necessary. At 211777 the foreshore exposes the pronounced F1 crush zone of the Niarbyl thrust or slide. F1 boudinage and lamination is deformed by small-scale F2 and F3 structures. The slide is at the contact of Lonan & Niarbyl Flags to the north and the Maughold Banded Pelites to the south, and unfortunately it cannot be traced inland, so that its full structural implications are unknown. The exposures on the foreshore show much shearing, crushing, boudinage and elongate "augen" structures. Patches crowded with minute garnets can be found in the Banded Pelites. Drive north to Peel Castle.

Locality I/10. Peel Castle. Drive along the west side of the harbour, past the castle entrance and park by the lifeboat station (242845). Walk through a small gateway through the castle wall and immediately on the seaward side is a shallow quarry just above high tide mark (242847). The floor of this shows folded Niarbyl Flags, which are here greywackes around 20-30 cm thick with pelite bands. The small F1 folds are upright and trend NE-SW: careful analysis of graded bedding is necessary to determine the position of anticlinal axes though at least one syncline is obvious (Figure 11). The fold axes are laterally offset by two small wrench faults, each of which houses a post-folding greenstone dyke. Whilst the fold axes are nearly horizontal in the quarry a traverse southwestwards along the path below the castle wall reveals folds in rather more pelitic beds plunging steeply to the southeast. Impressive views of the cliffs south of Peel may be had from the southern tip of the castle path; they are composed of the Niarbyl Flags for several kilometres. Continue along the path round the castle and back to the harbour.

Locality I/11. Ballanayre Strand. Roadside parking at Lynague Farm, midway between Peel and Kirkmichael (281868). Take the public footpath down to the north side of the headland at the north end of Ballanayre Strand. Turn to the left (south) through impressive sea-caves (low tide recommended); the cliffs and foreshore of Ballanayre Strand (279869) have fine sections in the Ballanayre Slump Breccia: this unusual rock is evidence of mass movement on the sea-floor of the type commonly known as olistostromes. The Slump Breccia is in apparent faulted contact with the Niarbyl Flags. Returning through the sea-caves a greenstone intrusion (much-altered dolerite) can be seen emplaced in much sheared Ladyport Banded Pelites on the north side of the headland. Return to the cars.

Locality I/12. Sulby Glen. The Sulby Slump Breccia is nowhere easy of access, though blocks are common on the beach east of Ramsey at about 457936. If in situ exposures are required, park in Sulby Glen (383925) and take the footpath along the east side of the Sulby River up into the Cluggid east bank tributary keeping to the north of the stream. The western slopes of The Cluggid, now partly clothed in the Ballakerka Plantation, have scattered crags some of which contain the Slump Breccia, particularly those adjacent to the Cluggid waterfall (390923). The Slump Breccia is also visible in the river bed below Tholt-y-Will and the east-bank tributary Block Eary around 381902 (loose blocks are common in the river bed adjacent to the confluence). Other outcrops of Slump Breccia are well hidden high in the western part of the Tholt-y-Will plantation (365898). Alternatively take the Druidale road from Ballaugh and crags of Slump Breccia are to be found (again well hidden by trees) near the road above Tholt-y-Will plantation (363897) and at the head of the Druidale stream (360882).

Locality I/13. Snaefell. Ample parking at The Bungalow where the Mountain Railway crosses the A18 road (395868). Take the footpath to the summit, crossing low crags of the Barrule Slates, with scattered quartz veining in harder beds. Minute garnets can be found in the slates at their highest metamorphic grade. The Mountain Railway cuttings provide loose material, but **Beware Trains!** On clear days Snaefell summit at 621 m provides views of Seven Kingdoms - Scotland (Southern Uplands and granites), England (the Lake District), Wales (Snowdonia), Ireland (the east Antrim coast and the Mourne Mountains), the Kingdom of Man, the Irish Sea (Kingdom of Neptune), and the Kingdom of God! The view also gives opportunity for considering the geological relationships of these to the Isle of Man, and for considering what may lie beneath the intervening sea. For example, where would you place the Iapetus suture?

Locality I/14. Port Mooar. Drive down the lane from Maughold village to Port Mooar shore at 487910. Take the footpath along the north side of the bay. A series of gentle north-south folds are developed in nearly flat-lying Lonan Flags, with nearly flat S2 cleavage. On turning the bend round the headland there are good views of Maughold Head whilst the rocks show a transition into the thinner Maughold Banded Pelites. With a steeper dip these are again cut by strong flat S2 cleavage (Fig. 14). Some pelitic bands have minute needles of tourmaline and spots of cordierite here in the metamorphic axis of the island. The first inlet north of Port Mooar Bay has an adit and other remains of iron mining and ore samples can be found on the beaches. Return to the cars.

II GRANITES AND MINES

The localities listed have been chosen to give a representative view of the two main granitic intrusions and the main groups of mines (Figures 2 and 19).

Locality II/1. Foxdale Granite & Spar quarry. From the village of Eairy take a minor road westwards for nearly a kilometre and park at the lane corner at the foot of the little used track up to the "spar" quarry (288777) (a left-hand track leads into a working quarry). An alternative approach may be made by a narrow lane branching south off the Eairy-Foxdale road at 288780. Walk up the track westwards and turn south into the quarry (288773). This is at the north end of a deep trench which extends southwards for nearly a kilometre across the heather-covered granite of Stone Mountain. The old part of the trench is overgrown and partly back-filled, whilst the present quarry gives magnificent exposures of granite, pegmatite and quartz veins (Figure 18). Such veins are "spar" in local usage. Part of the granite is deeply weathered and can be crumbled in the hand. Quartz separated from this is sometimes mixed with cement and used for brick-making - note the off-white bricks on building sites throughout the island. Pegmatites include several varieties of quartz-feldspar-mica intergrowths, some of them showing graphic texture. Vugs with free-grown crystals of quartz, orthoclase and both muscovite and biotite mica up to 2 cm wide are present. Quartz crystals up to 10 cm long occur sporadically, some of them with rose colouring. Rare occurrences of other minerals such as beryl have been recorded (Dawson, 1966; Simpson, 1966). Quartz and quartz-mica veins cut the pegmatites at various angles.

Continue into Foxdale village for views of various old mine buildings and waste heaps (the new school is built on a lead-mine waste heap!); the east-west vein has several shafts on it, the deepest being Beckwith's Shaft (282 780) going to a depth of 335 fathoms below surface (610 m), of which some 460 m are below sea-level. The vein continues beneath the northern flank of South Barrule into Glen Rushen (Figure 19).

Locality II/2. Glen Rushen Mines. Drive south from Foxdale village and turn west on A36 towards Round Table and Port Erin. After about 2 km turn off through a gate on the right close to a ruined mine engine house. The engine houses and waste heaps of Cross Shaft (263780) and Dixon's Shaft (267780) lie on the right but it is best to take the left fork in the track down to Beckwith's Mine (252778) (not to be confused with Beckwith's Shaft in Foxdale village), easily recognizable from its leaning chimney adjacent to the ruined engine house. These three mines are on the westerly continuation of the major east-west mineral vein through Foxdale and Glen Rushen. Extensive waste dumps provide samples of ore minerals, gangue and the slaty country rock. Immediately adjacent are the remains of the processing floors with much crushed waste, and wooden buddles and channels. Downhill to the west are the remains of a water-wheel housing and flat-rod system providing a power boost for pumping. In spite of numerous quarries in the Barrule Slates on the opposite hillside no evidence has been found of the vein continuing across to this western side of the valley.

Locality II/3. Bradda Head Mines. Drive to Port Erin and take the narrow lane behind the houses of Bradda West Road to the car park as in Locality I/5 above. Walk along contour path to the south foot of Bradda Head. A short length of zigzag track downhill below the fence takes one to a small ruined building from which one can view the relics of the South Bradda mine's engine house and chimney and the massive quartz vein behind (Figure 20). A dangerous scramble down the rocks gives access to these **but it is not recommended except for any but competent rock climbers.** The mine was worked well below sea-level and ore was shipped out by boat from the beach.

Return to the main path and climb Bradda Head; near the tower, waste material and rough ground mark the site of the former Spittals Shaft (185 699). Immediately to the north a shallow gully provides a view of the much mined north face of Bradda Head. It also marks the start of a very steep and dangerous path down to the shore. The North Bradda mines are concealed behind a small headland passable only at low tide. **(This path is not recommended for anyone not used to rough climbs).** Various adits go into the cliff face and a shaft was sunk to 72 fathoms (142 m) below sea-level. Return to the vehicles and drive across the island to Laxey. Note that around 100 other mine trials were made all over the island (Figure 19); few yielded more than a few tons of sulphide ores, and many were in barren quartz veins.

Locality II/4. Laxey Mines. From Laxey Village turn left on a well-signed road past the row of former miners' cottages and turn right up to the car park by the Lady Isabella Wheel (Figure 21) (coaches must park by the cottages). The mouth of the adit which extended northwards along the vein and intersected all the deep shafts can be seen low down near the river opposite the cottages en route. The Wheel was erected in 1852-4 to provide power via an underground water channel to work pumps in the Engine Shaft (235 fathoms; 460 m deep). Water was raised to adit level and flowed out to the valley side. There is a small admission charge to the Wheel and to a trail round other mining relics up the valley. Straight ahead is a small waterfall and traces of the vein may be seen in the river bed at low water; adjacent is a short adit which led to the Engine Shaft, and on the left is the viaduct carrying the flat-rod system for transmitting power from the wheel to the angle-bob over the shaft. Climb the trail on the right and it leads to the compressor house once powered by a water-turbine beneath. A short adit (access by prior arrangement with the Manx Museum) from the turbine leads into the side of Welch Shaft (the deepest at 271 fathoms; 530 m below adit level). Housed in the shaft here is the massive cylinder of the water-pressure engine which worked a "man-engine" taking the miners to and from work: they stepped on to platforms fixed to the rods and off again at the end of the stroke on to platforms fixed to the shaft side. Crossing to the west side of the valley the trail leads back to the crank side of the wheel. En route note the small reservoir for the water-supply to the wheel on the right. There is also a lane up to the village of Agneash where there was another deep shaft, now back-filled.

From the car park descend to the main road and take the side road opposite; this passes houses and gardens where there were ore-processing floors last century. Little is to be seen of these today. The Miners Inn adjacent to the railway station has various mining relics and old photos. Descend to Laxey Harbour: the ore concentrates were shipped out from here to the mainland for smelting, mostly before the present quay was built. On the beach many of the pebbles are rounded cobbles of both ore and waste from the mine and mineral samples may be obtained by cracking them (do not leave sharp bits of rock on the beach on account of danger to holiday-makers' feet). The amount of sphalerite and galena in the cobbles, and presumably in the sand, makes one wonder whether the sea-floor deposits below low tide mark might not be a potential ore reserve!

Locality II/5. Dhoon Granite. Park near the quarry entrance east of the Ramsey road (A2) (457871). The quarry only ceased working recently and permission must be sought in writing beforehand from Mr. L. Crellin at the Manx Department of Industry, Illiam Dhone House, Douglas. There is also a long disused and overgrown quarry on the other side (west) of the main road.

In the Dhoon granite quarry the details of what is visible have varied considerably as the faces advanced. In general the northern faces are the "type A granite" of Nockolds (1931) and the southern are "type B". Type A is a porphyritic microgranite with phenocrysts of opalescent quartz, orthoclase feldspar and biotite mica. Clusters of these give the rock a patchy appearance. Scattered groups of tourmaline needles can be found in some phenocryst patches. Type B is a darker, somewhat speckled rock with larger biotite phenocrysts. Xenoliths in various stages of digestion appear in both types, probably more common in type B which is closer to the margin of the intrusion. Thin-section and geochemical studies have revealed considerable variation in composition due to contamination by assimilation of xenoliths. The boundary between types A and B is gradational and Nockolds (1931) suggested that type B was the remnant of an earlier phase of intrusion. Joints in both types have scattered patches of molybdenite and pyrite. As at Foxdale some patches of the granite are deeply weathered and crumbly, particularly in the upper parts of the quarry face.

III   PEEL SANDSTONES

The itinerary provides an opportunity to study the varied fluvial facies totalling some 1000 m of probable Lower Old Red Sandstone age along a 2 km length of coast north of Peel (see Crowley, 1985, for details).

Locality III/1. Traie Fogog to the Stack. Park at the north end of Peel Promenade (250845) and take the footpath behind the swimming pool; the first outcrops seen above the pool are in sandstones of the Ballaquane Member. Continue over the headland and descend the steps into The Gob inlet at the south end of Traie Fogog bay by the ruined lido (251846) (Figure 23). Mid to low tide necessary.

A continuous section starts here in beds dipping seawards at about 45°. All the beds of this section represent low sinuosity alluvial fans with subtle differences indicating different parts of the channels and fan. They are well worth detailed study. The sequence exposed in The Gob starts with massive cyclic sandstones with mudstone-clasts in repeated channels comprising the Creg Malin Member. Turning the corner and passing a deep sea cave large expanses of bedding planes with mudstone intercalations make up the Traie Fogog Member. Ripple-marks and mega-ripples are present, together with desiccation cracks; sparse pedogenic calcretes appear near the foot of the second series of steps down the cliff. The north end of the Bay is in The Stack Member, a series of abundant pedogenic calcretes (=cornstones) (Figure 24) superimposed on mudstones, sandstones and conglomerates.

Return to the steps and rejoin the cliff-top path for about 200 m northeastwards. Opposite the isolated Stack, the seaward sloping cliff is in medium to coarse conglomerates with exotic cobbles. These include both rhyolitic volcanics and limestones with Silurian fossils derived from an unknown source, probably not more than about 10 km offshore. **(Parties visiting this exposure should take great care on the steep slope; hammering and collecting are discouraged).**

Either continue along the cliff-top path for 1.5 km and send vehicles round or return to the vehicles and drive northeast on the Kirkmichael road (A3) for a little over 2 km.

Locality III/2. White Strand and Wills Strand Bays. Park at the roadside by a small group of houses, one of which is a converted chapel

(268852) (Figure 52). Take the track between the houses and a path leads down to the beach (267854) close to a large erratic block of Carboniferous Limestone - where did it come from? Mid- to low tide is necessary for the rest of the section at this locality.

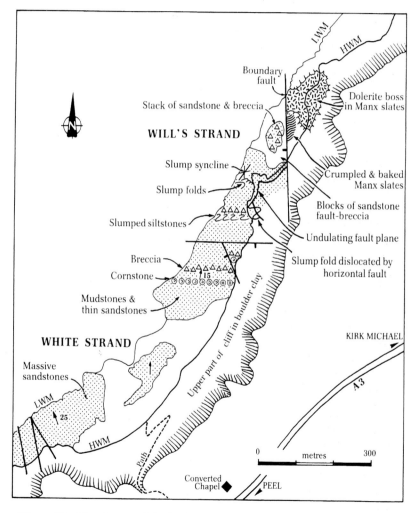

Figure 52: Sketch map of the Peel Sandstone Group in White Strand and Wills Strand bays (after Ford, 1972) (locality III/2).

The foreshore below modern beach level exposes fine conglomerates, sandstones, siltstones and mudstones of the Whitestrand Member dipping at 25-30° northwest. Where they are crossed by several small faults, cross the beach to the cliff foot, where fine conglomerates show pedogenic calcretes. The less calcreted beds yield scattered carbonate clasts which occasionally contain derived Upper Ordovician fossils.

At the headland at the northeast end of Whitestrand Bay (269859) a variety of syn-sedimentary disturbances are well-displayed (Ford, 1971) (Figure 52). They include minor overfolds (one with load structures on the undersurface), small scale "nappes" and thrusts, and other slump structures (Figures 25 & 26); all of these indicate movement of the sedimentary mass towards the present Manx massif, and they suggest that the Peel sandstone alluvial fan was unstable and perhaps dislodged by a penecontemporary earthquake off the present shore. The disturbed beds constitute the Wills Strand Member, the highest in the sequence. The largest and most impressive slump fold is in a small inlet in the middle of the headland, which also shows several faults associated with the boundary fault in Wills Strand. Beyond, at moderately low tide, it is possible to descend on to the shingle beach of Wills Strand (270860), and at low tide the foreshore shows crushed Peel sandstones in contact with the Lady Port Banded Pelites of the Manx Group. The headland at the northeast end of Wills Strand is a dolerite intrusion in the pelites and the contact between these and the dolerite can be followed in the cliff face.

The character of the conglomerates in the Peel Sandstone succession should be contrasted with the basal Carboniferous Langness Conglomerate seen in the next itinerary. They are very different and present no evidence for some previous writers, assignation of the Peel Sandstones to the Carboniferous.

Return via White Strand Bay to the vehicles.

IV CARBONIFEROUS LIMESTONE

This itinerary traverses sections through the Dinantian (Lower Carboniferous) strata along the south coast of the Isle of Man (Figure 27). Full details of the stratigraphy are given in Dickson, Ford & Swift (1987).

Locality IV/1. Langness. From Castletown drive to Derbyhaven, turn right and right again by a ruined building (formerly John Murrey's smelt house of 1711) and immediately left across the Golf Course on the lane leading to Langness lighthouse (as on Itinerary I/3) and park on the site of the old Langness copper mine (284659). Walk to the lighthouse, turn west for about 50 m and descend into Dreswick Harbour (282652) (Figure 53) . Both sides of this small inlet show coarse conglomerate resting unconformably on purple-stained and heavily brecciated (tropical weathering?) Lonan Flags division of the Manx Group (Figure 28). West of Dreswick Harbour the conglomerate still dips westwards but the Lonan Flags rise to form the western tip of the peninsula; this is partly due to faulting but it also suggests the presence of a former hill surrounded by a fluvial sheet flood deposit. Some masonry marks the former site of a trial shaft for copper ore. The conglomerate beds show much channelling with clasts being dominantly derived slabs from the Lonan Flags together with vein quartz; there are occasional sandy lenses and layers of mudstone flakes. Across the toe of the peninsula some 100 m northwest of the lighthouse the coast shows a fine section of the Langness Conglomerate eroded into pillars, stacks and arches close to the line of a north-south fault (282655). The interplay of the fault and unconformity yield some interesting relationships in the hollows by The Arches - a well-known local landmark. Also two of the inlets have Tertiary dolerite dykes in them. One inlet was extended as a trial adit for a copper mine without success. At the north end of The Arches traverse there is a dyke which changes its direction of dip markedly on passing from slate to conglomerate. Return to the vehicles and drive to the north end of the sea front at Derbyhaven.

Locality IV/2. Derbyhaven-Ronaldsway. Park at the end of the road 100m before the flying club (291 683). Continue along the foreshore below Ronaldsway airport (Figure 54). Mid- to low tide recommended. The section here is in the upper members of the Derbyhaven Formation, generally lenticular to undulating calcarenites with shale partings. The section extends for about 1 km and is rather broken up by faults and dykes, but interesting beds can be found with abundant *Michelinia* coralla, various trace fossils and scattered brachiopods. Near the light gantry a bedding surface shows fine mega-ripples (Figure 29). At the headland of Cass-ny-Hawin (298692) the limestone beds tilt up at the boundary fault against banded siltstones of the Lonan Flags well exposed south of the Santon River mouth. Climb to the cliff top and return to the vehicles. Drive round to Port St Mary.

Locality IV/3. Kallow Point, Port St Mary. Ample parking on the point adjacent to the harbour. Low tide recommended - the seaweed-covered rocks are very slippery in places. An embayment on the point shows an almost circular inlier of the highest Ballasalla Formation limestones (equivalent stratigraphically to the top of the Derbyhaven Formation but without a correlating marker horizon); they dip gently seawards. Just below the steps (212672) the ledges show the transition up into the base of the Castletown Formation. One ledge with a mass of bryozoa intertwined with trace fossils is taken as the boundary. Above

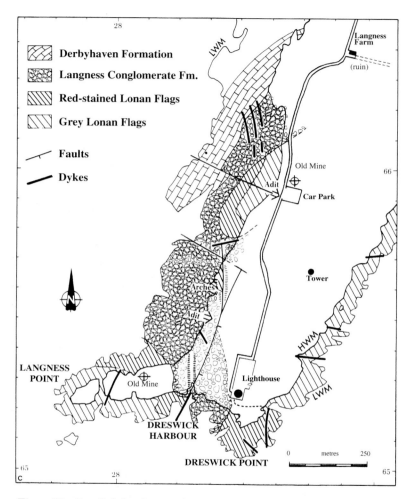

Derbyhaven Formation

Langness Conglomerate Fm.

Red-stained Lonan Flags

Grey Lonan Flags

Faults

Dykes

28

LWM

Langness
Farm

(ruin)

Old Mine

66

Adit

Car Park

Tower

Arches

Adit

HWM

LANGNESS
POINT

Old Mine

Lighthouse

LWM

DRESWICK
HARBOUR

N

0   metres   250

65

DRESWICK POINT

65

c

28

*Figure 53:   Detailed sketch maps for Itinerary IV - the Carboniferous
Limestone: (IV/1) the Langness Peninsula.*

the ledges is a bed with a very hummocky surface, each hummock being
an incipient concretion up to a metre across with a nucleus of piled-up
Zaphrentid corals (Figures 32 & 33). The same bed also has a scatter of
rounded quartz pebbles, presumably derived from the Manx Group
massif. The next beds above are full of *Zoophycos* trace fossils with
scattered large gastropods. The section can be followed round the point

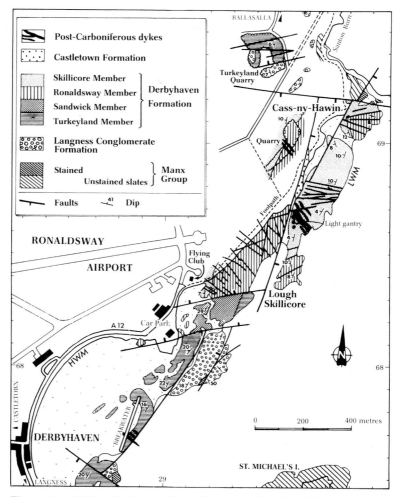

Figure 54: (IV/2). The Carboniferous Limestone of the Ronaldsway shore (after Dickson et al. 1987).

(with the remains of a lime kiln built into a mass of till resting on a striated limestone surface) for about 0.5 km to a boundary fault against intensely folded quartzitic beds in the Maughold Banded Pelites. The fault, with breccia once mistaken for Langness Conglomerate, can also be seen in the harbour floor at low tide. Return to the vehicles.

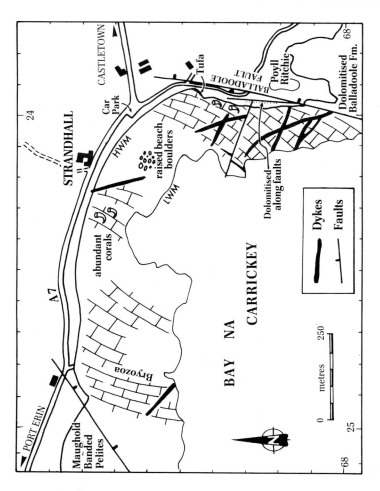

Figure 55: (IV/4). The Carboniferous Limestone of the Strandhall shore.

Locality IV/4. Strandhall to Poyll Ritchie. Limited parking at the east end of the sea wall (240686) near Strandhall Farm (Figure 55). Mid- to low tide necessary. Descend to the beach and walk to a point about 100 m west of Strandhall Farm. Bedding planes in the Castletown Formation, stratigraphically somewhat higher than the Port St Mary exposures, are well endowed with the giant Caninid coral *Siphonophyllia*, the large brachiopod *Megachonetes* and a scatter of compound coral colonies some of which are overturned. One of the *Siphonophyllia* is semi-circular having fallen over during growth and is over one metre long, perhaps the longest known rugose coral (Figure 31)! Traverse eastwards along the beach, noting the dykes across the bay and patches of cemented boulders from an old raised beach, as well as masses of tufa hanging from the low cliff (241684). Nearing Poyll Ritchie point the Balladoole Fault is marked by upturning and much dolomitization of the limestones. Vugs with dolomite crystals are common on the foreshore near the cottage (240683) and patches of pyrite crystals occur adjacent to where a dyke intersects the dolomitized fault zone. East of the fault the massive Balladoole limestones are much dolomitized, and so deeply corroded on the foreshore that it is difficult to determine the form of the heap of carbonate build-ups. These are better seen in the flooded Cross Welkin (= Fisher Hill) Quarry (247688) or the working Balladoole Quarry (245681) (Billown Quarries Ltd. near Ballasalla). (The adjacent Chapel Hill archaeological site is well worth a visit with its early Christian Keill (=chapel), Viking Ship Burial and Iron Age rampart - access from Balladoole lane at 248682). Bring cars up and park either on the grass opposite the entrance to Balladoole Quarry or, with permission, in Poyllvaaish farmyard. Walk to low cliff by Salt Spring Cottage.

Locality IV/5. Poyllvaaish to Close-ny-Chollagh. Low tide recommended when around Poyllvaaish Farm and Bay (Figure 56). The low cliff below Salt Spring Cottage shows the top of the Balladoole Formation, here thin black limestones with intercalated shales, locally developing build-ups with corals including *Lithostrotion portlocki* and clisiophyllids. They include some lenses of breccia probably resulting from debris flows. Overlying these are the shelly build-up limestones of the Poyllvaaish Formation. A traverse of these shows abundant brachiopods with scattered bivalves and gastropods in the lower build-ups (**No Hammering** - specimens available in beach shingle) giving way to abundant goniatites, particularly *Goniatites crenistria* in the higher beds. Descending into the Ghaw Gortagh inlet immediately northwest of the farm (245676), it is worth spending enough time to work out the relationships of every bed in the lower part of the Close-ny-Chollagh Formation, here banked against the highest Poyllvaaish Formation build-ups. The Close-ny-Chollagh beds comprise a series of fine-grained black shales and fine-grained dark limestones with sheets of coarser detritus; the latter often show grading and loading textures and are intercalated with breccia beds apparently representing debris flows. On the farm side of the inlet are a series of build-ups of light-coloured slightly shelly limestones which have foundered into the black beds with local contortion and irregular compaction of the latter (Figures 35 & 36). They appear to represent a former build-up complex south of the inlet which became unstable as the soft black muddy beds beneath

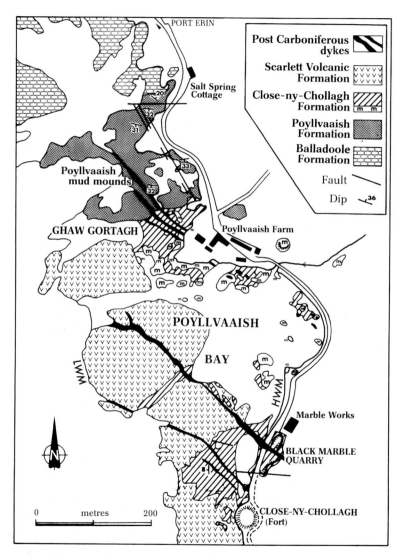

Figure 56: (IV/5). The Carboniferous Limestone of the Poyllvaaish area:
foundered blocks in the lower part of the Close-ny-Chollagh
Formation are indicated by the letter M (after Dickson et al.
1987).

compacted, and so broke up or even rotated into their present position. Three dolerite dykes cross the inlet (Figure 40).

Passing to the south of the farm the bay is floored by black limestones and shales of the upper part of the Close-ny-Chollagh Formation. These contain isolated lenses of brecciated build-up limestones, apparently once extensions of the southern complex. Near the marble works these beds are cut by a wide Tertiary dolerite dyke, also seen in the old quarry beyond the Marble Works (246672) (cut-off slabs of a variety of imported rocks can be found on the beach). Slabs of calcareous black shale at the south end of the quarry yield crushed fossil goniatites, posidonid bivalves and scraps of wood (Figure 34). Permission must be obtained from the marble works.

Descending to the foreshore the Close-ny-Chollagh Formation can be seen to be overlain by the lowest ash beds of the Scarlett Volcanic Formation, with some disturbance of the junction by irregular compaction (245671).

At this point it is worth by-passing the volcanics (Itinerary V) either by walking along the coast path to Scarlett Point, or by driving round through Castletown to the Scarlett Point car park.

Locality IV/6. Scarlett Point limestones. From Castletown square take the coast road southwest and park by the flooded Scarlett Quarry (259665) (Figure 57). The beds here should be compared with those traversed from Strandhall to Poyllvaaish. Immediately below the sea wall the Castletown Limestones are packed with *Siphonophyllia coralla*, many of them bent at odd angles owing to falling over when standing upright in a soft substrate. Walk south and by the Manx National Trust building (258664) descend immediately to the shore where the beds display a small monocline breached by erosion (Figure 30). Pits in the central bed have yielded fine specimens of the goniatite *Merocanites applanatus*, some of which can be seen in the Manx Museum. Return to the path and on climbing the stile a sequence of sweeping bedding planes demonstrates a fine series of small folds in the upper beds (Scarlett Point Member) of the Castletown Formation. One syncline is followed by a dyke. It is worth spending some time to work out the detailed relationships of outcrops in the inlet below the defunct Coastguard tower (257663). Beach shingle covers most of a fault zone in which two dykes are emplaced. Beyond the fault zone are highly dolomitized and somewhat brecciated Poyllvaaish limestones. At low tide thin black beds of the Balladoole Formation may be seen beneath these. Beyond the Poyllvaaish limestones a small fault brings in the Scarlett Volcanic Formation (see Itinerary V). The Close-ny-Chollagh Formation is cut out by the fault.

Return to the cars.

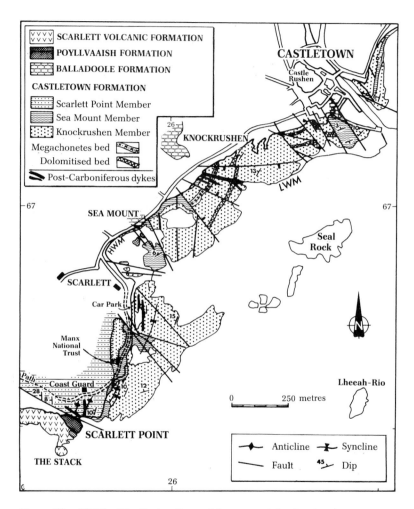

Figure 57: (IV/6). The Carboniferous Limestone of the Castletown to Scarlett Point shore (after Dickson et al. 1987).

V SCARLETT VOLCANICS

This short itinerary covers the upper Dinantian volcanic rocks occurring along some 1500 metres of coast between Close-ny-Chollagh Point in the north and Scarlett Point in the south (Figure 58). Most of the section is easily accessible from the coast path and the greater part is

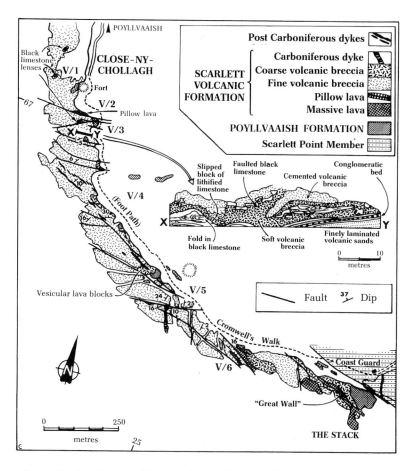

*Figure 58: Localities for Itinerary V - the Scarlett volcanics
(after Dickson et al. 1987).*

exposed even at high tide. It can be covered as a continuation walk from
Poyllvaaish or by parking at Scarlett and walking 1.5 km to the far end
of the section at Close-ny-Chollagh and turning back. The itinerary
provides an opportunity to see considerable variation in the detail and
character of a pile of basaltic volcanics. Unfortunately there is no clear
indication of whether one is doing a transect towards the centre of a
volcano, a tangential crossing of its flank or a random traverse of
volcanics derived from more than one vent. The largest proportion of

the volcanics is a fine hyaloclastic ash with scattered small volcani-clasts but there are also patches of a much coarser agglomerate, with clasts up to 0.5 m in diameter (Figure 37). Limestone clasts are sparsely distributed throughout and there is considerable alteration of the constituent minerals of the basalts. Small areas of interbedded fine-grained, dark, sometimes cherty limestones occur at several points.

Locality V/1: Close-ny-Chollagh. The basal contact of fine ash beds resting on black limestones can be seen below the ancient earthwork at Close-ny-Chollagh Point (246671). Here, compaction has resulted in several small domes of black limestone projecting up into the lowest ashes, some seen in section, and one in plan. In the cliff under the Point itself rather cherty black beds fill a hollow in the agglomerate surface and are themselves covered by more agglomerate with clasts of black cherty limestone. The volcanics extend across the seaward side of the bay to within about 5 m of one of the foundered limestone blocks.

Locality V/2. About 100 metres south of Close-ny-Chollagh Point, on the north side of a small inlet at 245670, a low cliff gives a fine section in pillow lavas (Figure 38). The floor of the adjacent inlet shows black limestone interbedded with ash.

Locality V/3. A further 100 metres south, in the next inlet, (245668) there is a complex section showing volcanic sands overlain by a thin conglomerate of limestone and basalt boulders; in turn this is capped with a slumped horizon of soft ash with included limestone lenses and boulders, finally capped with more volcanic breccias; at the seaward end these include a large slipped block of limestone and contorted thin black beds. The sequence suggests the former presence of a submarine slide of volcanic and marine deposits.

Locality V/4. The next 300 metres are fine agglomerates, and on climbing the next stile (247667) there is a low cliff of very coarse agglomerate with most of the clasts being vesicular basalt, some suggestive of the skins of pillows, possibly the result of a lava flow disrupted by a steam explosion. Two Tertiary dolerite dykes cut the agglomerate here.

Locality V/5. The next 300 metres have a scatter of large limestone blocks in fine agglomerate and at 249655 a contemporary dyke cuts the agglomerate.

Locality V/6. Cromwell's Walk. On reaching Cromwell's Walk, marked by a massive stone wall along the landward side of the path (252663) blocks from a massive vesicular basaltic lava flow overlie coarse agglomerate.

Locality V/7. After a further 300 metres, at 255663, a patch of lava with the odd feature of vertical bands of vesicles outcrops in the grassy hollow adjacent to the path; another is to be found at the seaward edge of the exposures. Immediately south of these a "great wall" of lava appears cutting through the agglomerates for some 200 metres towards the Stack of Scarlett (256662) (Figure 39). This wall has poorly developed ropy (pahoehoe) surfaces on both sides in places, possibly due to squeeze-up features rather than former flow surfaces. The wall and coarse agglomerates extend to the Point, being faulted against dolomitized Poyllvaaish limestones near the Coastguard tower. At the point itself The Stack shows poorly developed radial columnar structures, suggesting that it might have occupied a vent. The Stack can be reached by a slippery traverse over seaweed-covered rocks at low tide only.

On leaving the volcanics and returning to the car park it is worth pondering that these are the youngest Carboniferous rocks on the south coast, so how far do they extend offshore and what lies beyond? Millstone Grit and Coal Measures? Offshore drilling has revealed that the eastern Irish Sea covers a deep Millstone Grit (Namurian) basin.

VI   TERTIARY DYKES

This short itinerary is separately given for those interested in Tertiary igneous activity, but for non-specialists it is recommended that the topic can be covered adequately during Itinerary IV on the Carboniferous Limestone. Most of the dykes noted at Localities VI/3 to VI/6 are clearly visible cutting Carboniferous Limestone but those cutting the Lonan Flags of the Manx Group on the east side of Langness are less obvious as they have weathered back into recesses.

Locality VI/1. Port Mooar, Maughold Head. The dykes here and at Dhyrnane are probably the most easily accessible examples within the Manx Slate. Port Mooar is accessible by car down a narrow lane off the Ballajora road south of Maughold village: otherwise park in the village and walk down a little over 1 km. Cross to the south side of the bay (487906) and both foreshore and cliff have a 3 m wide dyke trending NW-SE.

Locality VI/2. Dhyrnane, Maughold Head. Dhyrnane is a small inlet some 400 m northeast of Port Mooar accessible on foot via a narrow lane from the east end of Maughold village or by the coastal footpath from Port Mooar bay. There are two dykes each about a metre wide one on the west side of the inlet and another about 100 m further south. Haematite veins occur along the contacts of some dykes.

Locality VI/3. Strandhall to Poyllvaaish. A traverse of the Carboniferous Limestone beds of this coast has been described in

Trevor D. Ford

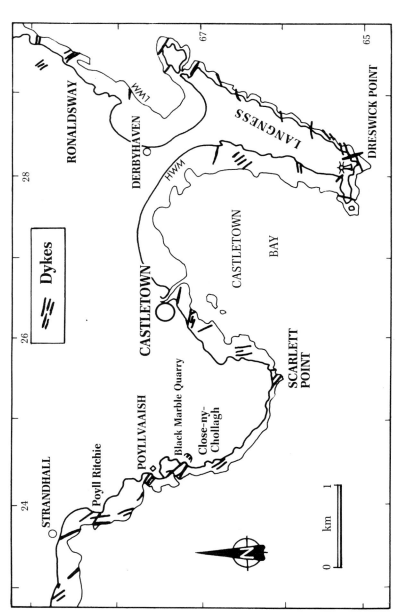

Figure 59: Localities for Itinerary VI – the Tertiary dykes of the Castletown coast.

Itinerary IV and the sketch maps (Figures 55, 56 & 57) show several of the dykes. These and others are emphasized on Figure 59. At low tide the foreshore southeast of Kentraugh House (228068) two NNW dykes 30 and 60 cm wide are visible, but often hidden in seaweed, cutting older Caledonian dykes in Manx Slate adjacent to the Carboniferous boundary fault.

The foreshore immediately below Strandhall (238686) has a 3 m wide dyke cutting Castletown Limestones. It has bands of amygdules parallel to the walls. The opposite side of the Bay, west of Poyll Ritchie Cottage (240 683) has two dykes, each about 0.5 m wide, showing mutual cross-cutting relationships. Two more, each about 0.5 m wide, are present immediately east of the Balladoole Fault near low water mark south of Poyll Ritchie, and there is another in Balladoole Quarry.

Immediately west of Poyllvaaish Farm, three dykes, each about 0.5 m wide, cross Ghaw Gortagh inlet (244676) (Figure 40). In Close-ny-Chollagh Bay immediately west of the "marble" quarry (246672) two dykes, about 12.5 and 0.5 m wide converge eastwards, and appear to merge into the single dyke in the quarry itself. Seawards, both of these cut the Scarlett Volcanics near low tide mark. Two more dykes also cut the volcanics some 500 m to the south (248665).

Locality VI/4. Scarlett Point. A dyke some 60 cm wide cuts the limestones along a synclinal axis below the Coastguard Tower (257662) (Figure 57). Another, little over 10 cm wide, cuts the same limestones along the northeast side of the inlet, whilst another, largely covered by beach boulders, is about 2-3 m wide along the southwest side of the inlet.

Locality VI/5. Langness. Several narrow dykes occur on the foreshore west of the car park (283 661); two more occur in the vicinity of The Arches (Figure 53). One cuts both Langness Conglomerate and the underlying Lonan Flags, showing a change in direction of dip in passing from slate to conglomerate. Another NNW dyke cutting the Manx Group (Lonan Flags) crosses Tobacco Gullet immediately east of the lighthouse (284652). Others can be found in the various "gullets" on the east side of Langness though they tend to be weathered back and concealed by turf or seaweed.

Locality VI/6. Ronaldsway. Three dykes trending NW-SE each a metre or so in width cut the limestones by the airport light gantry (296687); one of them cuts the Skillicore fault. Three more dykes are close together in the adjacent quarry (296689) (Figure 54).

VII   QUATERNARY OF THE NORTHWEST COAST

The two magnificent coastal sections through late Pleistocene deposits are each worthy of a full day's excursion so they are treated separately here. Apart from the extreme southern end the deposits seen all rest on around 50 m of earlier Pleistocene deposits now known only from boreholes below sea level. Those visible in the cliffs are all Devensian in age, probably mostly late Devensian. They demonstrate the effects of repeated advances and retreats of the ice sheets, and are capped by post-glacial sediments in places. The sections of the northwest coast are cut oblique to the trend of the Bride moraine and are dominated by outwash materials. Glacio-tectonic effects are not seen in contrast to the northeast coast (see Itinerary VIII). The interplay between the bulk of the deposits originating from Scottish ice advancing southwards on to the Isle of Man and limited sheets of material derived from the Manx uplands is evident. Details of the deposits and their stratigraphic relationships with the northeast coast are given in the various pubications by G.Thomas (1976, 1977) and R.V.Dackombe & G. Thomas (1985), on whose work these itineraries are based.

The Itinerary may be done by walking some 14 km of almost continuous section along the coast with a pick-up by transport at the end, or a less energetic method would be to visit only the localities noted below (Figures 60 & 61). Mid to low tide is recommended, though most sections are accessible at all but high spring tides. Visits during strong onshore weather would also be uncomfortable. Afternoon visits are recommended for photography.There is parking for cars and minibuses at all localities, though it is not possible to take coaches down some of the narrow lanes.

Locality VII/1. Glen Mooar. Starting from Kirkmichael drive 2 km south on the A3 road to Peel and turn right down a narrow lane and through a ford to the car park by the shore (302 894). The section visible hereabouts is:-

Ballaleigh Debris Fan - a scree of mostly local material

Trunk Till - a thin flow till from the ice surface

Orrisdale Sands - thick outwash from the Orrisdale advance

Orrisdale Till - thin representative of a major till sheet

Mooar Head - solifluction deposit

Wyllin Till - a lodgement till

Mooar Scree - frost-shattered Manx slate debris

Manx Group - frost-shattered in upper layers

The top three units are easily accessible in a sandy gulley opposite the car park. Some periglacial features are present in the top layers, suggesting cross-sections of frost polygons.

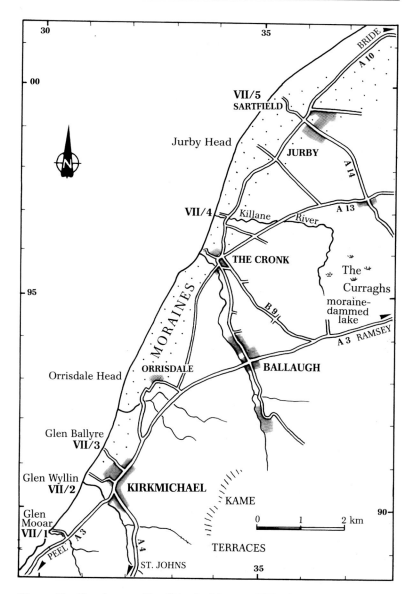

Figure 60: Sketch map of localities for Itinerary VII - the Quaternary deposits of the northwest coast.

On leaving the gulley turn left (south) along the beach for about 170 metres to the first appearance of the Manx Group at the cliff foot and the rest of the section can be seen either directly above or on the return northwards.

Return to the vehicles and drive round to Glen Wyllin.

Locality VII/2. Glen Wyllin. On driving back towards Kirkmichael take a narrow lefthand lane into Glen Wyllin at 314902 about 300 m south of the main road junction. Drive down past the pleasure grounds and park near the shore (310906). On the beach turn left (south) and the Orrisdale Till is seen close to the cliff foot. Unconformably beneath it are the Wyllin Till and associated outwash sands; the latter yield numerous specimens of the gastropod *Turritella* and a few other shells, either dredged up from the sea floor north of the island, or deposited in a marine incursion along the ice margin. A section in the Orrisdale Sands, here with gravel spreads, is capped by Trunk Till and the slate scree of the Ballaleigh Debris Fan. Return to the Glen mouth noting the uneven till base and its contact with the underlying till or sand (often obscured by cliff fall material). The north bank of the stream shows good varved silts and muds, and a few metres further north are blocks of concrete resulting from a cottage undermined by marine erosion in the last 20 years. About 100 m metres further north there is a complex of infilled kettles holes seen in section in the upper half of the cliff. The fill comprises about 2 m of Chara marl capped by organic-rich peaty clays which were deposited in a pond where a stranded lump of ice melted after the rest of the glacier wasted away (Figure 50). Dates of around 11000 BP have been obtained by radiocarbon dating. The lower half of the cliff is mostly Orrisdale Sands. Return to the vehicles.

Locality VII/3. Glen Ballyre. In Kirkmichael turn down the lane some 200m north of the church to reach the shore at 313914. Turn right (north) along the beach for about 150 metres. The section here shows Orrisdale Till at the cliff foot, (often obscured by fallen debris) and the overlying masses of gravel interfinger laterally with sands on both sides suggesting the former positions of outwash streams. The sands are locally cemented and weird eroded slabs can be found on the beach. The cliff is capped with Trunk Till and two more kettle holes, one of which has been dated at about 18000 years BP. Windblown sands cap the cliff. This section continues past Glen Trunk (316 923) for 1.5 km to Orrisdale Head where most of the cliff is a mass of Orrisdale Sands and Gravels, representing the core of the Bride moraine (Figure 45). The Orrisdale Till gradually dips below beach level. Return to the vehicles.

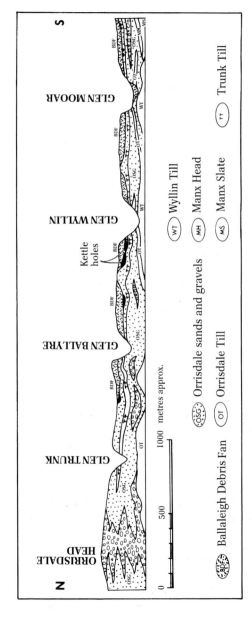

Figure 61: Diagrammatic section of the glacial and associated deposits visible in the cliffs of the northwest coast (after Thomas, 1977).

Locality VII/4. Killane River mouth. From Kirkmichael take the main road towards Ballaugh. On leaving Kirkmichael kame terraces are visible to the right on the slope rising to the slate uplands. Continue into Ballaugh and turn left on to A10 for Jurby. After about 4 km park at the roadside adjacent to the mouth of the Killane River (342968), which drains part of the former Curragh Lake. Walk down a track to the beach and turn right (north) (340970). About 400 metres north the Orrisdale Till rises from beneath beach level; above it is a much reduced Orrisdale Sand, covered by the Jurby Till, not seen before, and its cover of Jurby Sands. On returning to the Killane River mouth, to the south is a low cliff section in post-glacial sands with some contortion due to ice heave. Return to the vehicles.

Locality VII/5. Sartfield. From Killane drive 3 km to the Jurby crossroads and turn left (northwest) to the hamlet of Sartfield; park adjacent to the sewage works and walk to the beach (352998). Turn left (southwest) passing periglacial cryoturbation involutions in the uppermost beds and walk towards Jurby Head for about 600 metres. The section here is Orrisdale Till at beach level covered by Orrisdale Sands and Gravels, a thick Jurby Till, and Jurby Sands. After a further 300 m (348992) the Orrisdale Till is below beach level but an upward intrusion of a boulder train has penetrated the Sands and Gravels (Figure 46). Seen as an inverted L-shape in the cliff this is composed of Carboniferous Limestone blocks up to 1m diameter with limited till matrix emplaced in the Orrisdale Sands; the limestone blocks may have been scraped up from beneath the glacial succession or they may be far-travelled from Scotland, but either way their method of emplacement gives rise to speculation.

Locality VII/6. Blue Point. Continue north on the A10 road towards Bride for 5 km and then take the lane northwest to the car park at Blue Point (NX 394026). The point marks the start of the post-glacial (Flandrian) cliff line cut into the upstream face of the Bride moraine and of the shingle ridges system of The Ayres. Coastal sand dunes parallel the beach.

Locality VII/7. The Ayres. Continue along the A10 road towards Bride for some 4 km and turn left (north) to the Manx National Trust site and visitor centre for The Ayres. Though containing a few wartime concrete installations, this area has been protected from the ravages of gravel extraction and provides a pleasant nature trail walk across the varied physical and vegetation features of the shingle ridge and dune terrane.

If time and energy permit, complete the northwest coast traverse with a visit to the Point of Ayre - see locality VIII/6 in the next itinerary.

VIII   QUATERNARY OF THE NORTHEAST COAST

The object of this excursion is a traverse along the northeast coast
through the Pleistocene deposits banked against the Manx Slate uplands
at Ramsey northwards across the sandur (= outwash plain) to the Bride
moraine, with its glacio-tectonic phenomena and beyond to the
Holocene deposits at the northern tip of the Isle of Man (Figures 62 &
63).

Locality VIII/1. Ballure, Ramsey. Park near the pier at Ramsey
(456939) or on the terrace at 457936 and walk southeast along the
beach for about 400 m until a cliff section in tills and sands is seen just
beyond the mouth of Ballure Glen. Mid to low tide recommended.

At the south end of the Ballure section a coarse scree of slate
fragments is banked against the Manx Group and draped across a small
cave. This has been excavated unsuccessfully in the hope of finding
interglacial deposits. Above the Manx Group is a sequence of 14 units
of Pleistocene deposits:-

14. Ballure Clays

13. Ballure Debris Fan

12. Ballure Clays

11. Ballure Debris Fan

10. Ballure Clays.

9. Ballure Debris Fan

8. Shellag Till (seen only on foreshore)

7. Ballure Till

6. Upper Blue Head

5. Shellag Sand

4. Lower Brown Head

3. Ballure Slope wash

2. Brown Head

1. Ballure Scree

The section demonstrates the effect of glaciers from the north
yielding exotic mainly fine-grained materials which alternate with slaty
debris fans and gravels derived by solifluction and slope wash from the
Manx Group uplands to the south. The three layers of head are local
material whilst the intervening Shellag Sand appears to be outwash from
an ice margin to the north. This is capped by till, and the final five units
are an interdigitation of local screes with the fine-grained sediments of
the sandur spreading south from the Bride moraine 7 km to the north.
Return to the vehicles.

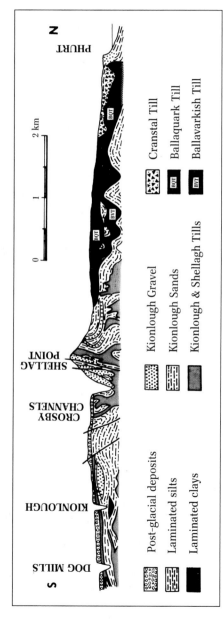

Figure 63: Diagrammatic section of the glacial and associated deposits of the northeast coast (after Thomas, 1976, 1977).

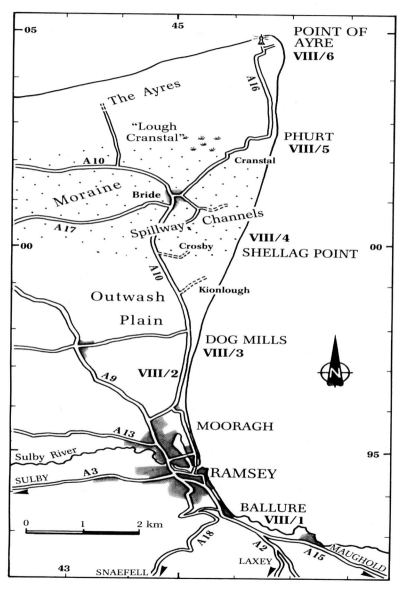

Figure 62: Sketch map of localities for Itinerary VIII - the Quaternary deposits of the northeast coast.

Trevor D. Ford

Locality VIII/2. Mooragh: Drive north through Ramsey to the north (Mooragh) promenade. On the left (west) of this at about 450953 a low cliff rises above the level of the promenade and appears to represent the Flandrian high sea-level of the post-glacial. From the north end of the promenade the section may be done by walking the whole 7 km of beach to Phurt but a less energetic method is to visit the localities noted below.

Drive northwards for 2.5 km to Dog Mills.

Locality VIII/3. Dog Mills. Park at the roadside - clear of the blind bend! Walk down the short track to the beach. Mid to low tide recommended. Turn right (south) for about 40 metres (453978). The low cliff here is composed of outwash deposited in standing water at the margin of the sandur. Shellag Till is sometimes exposed on the foreshore at low water. The cliff is composed of silts and clays exhibiting numerous load structures such as ball and pillow, with sandy lobes projecting downwards from the base of the thicker sand layers, and flame structures of clay extending upwards into overlying silts (Figure 49). Some of the layers have yielded foraminifera indicating that the environment was an embayment of the sea rather than part of the Curragh Lake as once supposed.

In the next kilometre to the north there is much more sand and some gravel as one approaches the moraine; around Kionlough (455986) a sheet of till occupies part of the cliff. Return to the vehicles or continue walking north to Shellag Point.

Locality VIII/4. Shellag Point. Spectacular glacio-tectonic sections but a little difficult of access! Either walk along the whole 6 km of section from Dog Mills and arrange to meet transport at Phurt (467028) or drive to Phurt and walk back to Shellag Point, 2.5 km each way. The drive through Bride village crosses the massive hummocky moraine, with numerous spillway channels now seen as dry valleys, before descending to the north across the swampy former site of the moraine-dammed Lake Cranstal (NX4502) to the dunes and shingle of the Ayres at Phurt. Small groups may park (after obtaining permission) at Crosby Farm (452998) or at Kionlough (456993) and walk across the fields to the cliff top and descend by a steep scramble down a gulley at SC459999. Either return the same way or send transport on to Phurt and walk northwards along the beach. Mid to low tide essential. Morning visits are recommended to get the sun on the cliff sections.

At Shellag Point, to the south of the obvious gulley the section is mainly in steeply inclined outwash sands with thin till sheets, repeated by thrust faults. The main section is to the north of the gulley where Shellag Till is seen in the foreshore, with low ridges marking the positions of thrusts below beach level. The cliff above (Figure 47) is some 80 m high and has three main stratigraphic units (though with the glacio-tectonics these may appear in any order!):-

Kionlough Gravel
Kionlough Sands
Kionlough Till (merging with Shellag Till in the beach)

These are highly deformed: isoclinal folds are cut by thrust and reverse faults at various angles. Vertical strata are common and being unconsolidated today, they must have been frozen to fold in such a manner, whilst being pushed up by a late re-advance of the ice. Near the cliff top they are unconformably overlain by horizontal wind-blown sands. The main highly deformed section lasts only for some 200m; beyond, to the north, the deformation is less intense but an upper sheet of Ballavarkish Till discordantly transects the folds in the lower beds about in the middle of the cliff (Figure 48). About one kilometre to the north this till is in turn transgressed by the still higher Ballaquark Till with a less obvious discordance. Both these till sheets have sand and gravel lenses probably representing englacial stream channels. Towards the northern end of the section sheets of outwash sand and gravel are associated with the Ballaquark Till. A 'fossil forest' of ancient tree stumps projects through beach sands near low water mark.

Locality VIII/5. Phurt. In the low cliff at Phurt (NX 467027) directly beneath the eroded end of the side road (and sometimes partly concealed by rubbish) is a section in post-glacial lake deposits about 4 m thick. Of Boreal/Atlantic transition age, the organic-rich silts and clays yield abundant *Equisetum* remains as well as other macro-plants, pollen and occasional Neolithic flint implements. These sediments rest in a small basin in the top of the Ballaquark Till, as occasionally seen in foreshore exposures amongst beach cobbles. Two other similar basins are less well exposed in the next 100 m of low cliff to the north. Return to the vehicles.

Locality VIII/6. Point of Ayre. Drive 2 km almost to the lighthouse. Take the lane to the right and park at the end about 300 m east of the lighthouse (NX 467049) (Figure 44). The last kilometre or so of road crosses a series of thinly vegetated raised beach storm ridges composed of coarse shingle, exploited nearby for commercial gravel. The shingle deposits forming currently and formed in the recent past constitute massive ridges between the lighthouse and the present shore. The pebbles have been derived by the erosion of the "drift" on the sea floor north of the island and by long-shore drift from the eroding moraines on both coasts before being thrown up by storms. It is worth a hand-lens petrographic examination of the pebbles, particularly when wet at the water's edge. Many are flint, presumably derived from Chalk outcrops on the sea-floor northeast of Ireland, whilst others provide a representative selection of Southern Uplands granites and greywackes and of western Scottish igneous rocks. Common amongst the latter are pebbles with characteristic blue spots, which are riebeckite microgranite derived from Ailsa Craig in the Firth of Clyde, their abundance suggesting that that islet was once a very much larger intrusion. On clear days Scotland, Ireland and the Lake District are clearly visible and give rise to speculation as to the nature of the sea-floor geology beneath the northern Irish Sea. Below sea level at the Point of Ayre are 126 m of pre-Devensian deposits, including thick fossiliferous marine clays and silts.

A few blocks of concrete at the Point of Ayre are all that survives of the former brine-pumping industry active around 1900. Boreholes penetrated some 800 m of Permo-Triassic mudstones with halite beds resting on thick sandstones beneath the drift; brine was pumped out of the halite beds and to Ramsey through a pipeline unwisely laid at the cliff foot, where it was soon breached by storm waves.

As the Cumbrian coalfield extends out beneath the sea towards the Isle of Man there has been an intermittent search for an equivalent coalfield beneath The Ayres, so far without success.

REFERENCES

ALLEN, J.R.L. & CROWLEY, S.F. 1983. Lower Old Red Sandstone fluvial dispersal systems in the British Isles. *Transactions of the Royal Society of Edinburgh, Earth Science,* **74**, 61-68.

BOLTON, H. 1899. The palaeontology of the Manx Slate of the Isle of Man. *Memoirs & Proceedings of the Manchester Literary & Philosophical Society,* **43**, 1-15.

BROWN, P.E., MILLER, J.A. & GRASTY, R.L. 1968. Isotopic ages of late Caledonian granitic intrusions in the British Isles. *Proceedings of the Yorkshire Geological Society ,* **36**, 261-276.

CARRUTHERS, R.G. & STRAHAN, A. 1923. *Lead and Zinc ores of Durham, Yorkshire, Derbyshire and the Isle of Man.* Geological Survey Special Reports on Mineral Resources, **26**, IOM, pp. 89-91.

CORNWELL, J.D. 1972. A gravity survey of the Isle of Man. *Proceedings of the Yorkshire Geological Society,* **39**, 93-106.

COWIN, F. & SCARFFE, A. undated. *c.* 1991. *Lady Isabella and the Great Laxey Mine.* Manx Museum and National Trust Guide Book. 36pp.

CROWLEY, S.F. 1985. Lithostratigraphy of the Peel Sandstones, Isle of Man. *Mercian Geologist,* **5**, 499-512.

DACKOMBE, R.V. & THOMAS, G.S.P. 1985. *Field Guide to the Quaternary of the Isle of Man.* Quaternary Research Assoc., Cambridge. 122pp.

DAWKINS, W.BOYD, 1902. The red sandstones of Peel, Isle of Man. *Quarterly Journal of the Geological Society, London,* **58**, 633-646.

DAWSON, J. 1966. *Beryllium in the Foxdale Granite, Isle of Man.* Bulletin of the Geological Survey of Great Britain. No.25, 55-58.

DICKSON, J.A.D., FORD, T.D. & SWIFT, A. 1987. The stratigraphy of the Carboniferous rocks around Castletown, Isle of Man. *Proceedings of the Yorkshire Geological Society,* **46**, 203-229.

DOWNIE, C. & FORD, T.D. 1966. Microfossils from the Manx Slate Series. *Proceedings of the Yorkshire Geological Society,* **35**, 307-322.

EYLES, C.H. & EYLES, N. 1984. Glaciomarine sediments of the Isle of Man as a key to Late Pleistocene stratigraphic investigations in the Irish Sea basin. *Geology,* 12, 359-364.

FORD, T.D. 1972. Slump structures in the Peel Sandstones Series, Isle of Man. *Isle of Man Natural History & Antiquarian Journal,* VII, (3), 440-448.

GARRAD, L.S., BAWDEN, T.A., QUALTROUGH, J.K., & SCATCHARD, W.J. 1972. *The Industrial Archaeology of the Isle of Man.* David & Charles, Newton Abbot. 266pp.

HARPER, C.T. 1966. Potassium-argon ages of slates from the southern Caledonides of the British Isles. *Nature,* **212,** 1339-1341.

HELM, D.G., ROBERTS, B. & SIMPSON, A. 1963. Polyphase folding in the Caledonides south of the Scottish Highlands. *Nature,* **200,** 1060-1062.

HOLLIS, D.B. 1987. *The forgotten iron mines of Kirk Maughold, Isle of Man.* British Mining (Memoirs of the Northern Mines Research Society) No.34, 46-54 (see also British Mining No.37, 4-15, 1988).

INESON, P.R. & MITCHELL, J.G. 1979. K-Ar ages from the ore deposits and related rocks of the Isle of Man. *Geological Magazine,* 116, 117-128.

LAMPLUGH, G.W. 1903. *The Geology of the Isle of Man.* Mem. Geol. Surv. England & Wales. 620pp.

LEWIS, H.P. 1930. The Avonian succession in the south of the Isle of Man. *Quarterly Journal of the Geological Society, London,* **86,** 234-288.

MOLYNEUX, S. 1980. New evidence for the age of the Manx Group, Isle of Man. pp. 415-421 in *The Caledonides of the British Isles - Reviewed.* A.L.Harris, C.H.Holland & B.E.Leake (editors), Geological Society, London.

NOCKOLDS, S.R. 1931. The Dhoon (Isle of Man) granite: a study in contamination. *Mineralogical Magazine,* **22,** 494-509.

QUIRK, D.G., FORD, T.D., KING, J.A., ROBERTS, I.L., POSTANCE, R.B., & ODELL, I. 1990. Enigmatic boulders and syn-sedimentary faulting in the Carboniferous Limestone of the Isle of Man. *Proceedings of the Yorkshire Geological Society,* **48,** 99-113.

ROBERTS, B., MORRISON, C., & HIRONS, S. 1990. Low grade metamorphism of the Manx Group, Isle of Man: a comparative study of white mica 'crystallinity' techniques. *Journal of the Geological Society, London,* **147,** 271-277.

ROBINSON, V. & McCARROLL, D. 1990. *The Isle of Man: celebrating a sense of place.* Liverpool University Press, 289pp.

SIMPSON, A. 1963a. The stratigraphy and tectonics of the Manx Slate Series, Isle of Man. *Quarterly Journal of the Geological Society, London,* **119,** 367-400.

SIMPSON, A. 1963b. Quartz veining in the Manx Slate Series. *Nature,* **199,** 900-901.

SIMPSON, A. 1964a. The metamorphism of the Manx Slate Series. *Geological Magazine,* 101, 20-36.

SIMPSON, A. 1964b. Deformed acid intrusions in the Manx Slate Series, Isle of Man. *Geological Journal,* 4, 189-206.

SIMPSON, A. 1965. The syn-tectonic Foxdale-Archallagan granite and its metamorphic aureole. *Geological Journal,* 4, 415-434.

SIMPSON, A. 1966. Summer field meeting in the Isle of Man. *Proceedings of the Geologists Association,* 77, 217-227.

SIMPSON, A. 1968. The Caledonian history of the north-eastern Irish Sea region and its relation to surrounding areas. *Scottish Journal of Geology,* 4, 135-163, with discussion on pp. 375-385.

SKELTON, R.H. 1956. The Manx Mines. *Mining Magazine,* 9-18.

TAYLOR, J.H. & GAMBA, E.A. 1933. The Oatland igneous complex, Isle of Man. *Proceedings of the Geologists Association,* 44, 355-376.

THOMAS, G.S.P. 1976. The Quaternary Stratigraphy of the Isle of Man. *Proceedings of the Geologists Association,* **87.** 307-323.

THOMAS, G.S.P. 1977. The Quaternary of the Isle of Man. pp.155-178 in *The Quaternary History of the Irish Sea* editor G.H.Mitchell, Geological Journal Special Issue no.7, Liverpool.

THOMAS, G.S.P., CONNAUGHTON, M. & DACKOMBE, R.V. 1985. Facies variation in a Late Pleistocene supraglacial outwash sandur from the Isle of Man. *Geological Journal,* 20, 193-213.

TOOLEY, M. 1978. Flandrian sea-level changes and vegetational history of the Isle of Man: a review. In *Man and the environment in the Isle of Man.* edited by P.Davey, British Archaeological Reports **54,** Oxford.

WARD, C. 1970. The Ayres raised beach, Isle of Man. *Geological Journal,* 7, 217-220.

NOTES